readers write about this book

SIMPLE AND DIRECT

"This was the simplest, most direct and easily understandable presentation on the subject of Shiatsu that I have encountered. The Behavioral Kinesiology was most enlightening. This applies both to your lecture/demonstration and your book."

June Silverman, Supervisor,
Therapeutic Nursing Program
N.Y.U. - Bellevue Medical Center

IMMEDIATE RESULTS

"Your book is indeed a joy and a handbook for what ails a body (and mind!). The Shiatsu does the trick for sinus headaches and your instructions for meditation are concise: the kind of instructions that bring about immediate results. The beauty of your book is its simplicity and workability."

B. T., Pittsburgh, PA

OFFERS MUCH

"Jerry is dedicated to caring healing, and does his homework well and professionally. His is a quiet strength. His book offers much and it works."

Robert Dean Meridith, Former Dean
School of Planning and Architecture
Pratt Institute

SLEEPING BETTER

Read your book regularly and am sleeping better. My mind is relaxed and I can tell when my muscles are tense. Then I think of a beautiful place and before I know it I'm fast asleep."

P.P., Denver, CO

MANY WILL FIND IT USEFUL

"Your book is excellent. We have enjoyed it very much and are sure many will find it useful also."

Pat
Sout   itute

D1288441

more reader comments

BEST RELAXATION IN YEARS

"My husband came home from work with a severe headache. He rarely gets one, and this was a dilly. He went straight to bed, but three hours later it was just as bad.

"Then I remembered an article on shiatsu ("Push Here for Pain Relief," an article about Jerry Teplitz which appeared in *Prevention*, April 1980) and the pressure points for treating a headache. I followed the diagram and the results were amazing. After one "treatment," his headache felt much better. He said he had a tingly sensation all the way down to his toes. He got up and ate dinner. Then I gave him one more treatment and his headache was gone. He asked me to do it again because he said it felt so good—he hadn't been that relaxed in years. All from touching a few spots on his head! The next morning he woke up feeling great."

Heather Hagaman, Flagstaff, Arizona
(Reprinted from *Prevention,* Feb. 1981)

HELPS ME SLEEP

"I have begun to relax and enjoy! I like your book. I used it just the other night to learn about a tea to help me to sleep and it worked.

D.W., San Diego, CA

REALLY IMPRESSED!

"I read your book—really impressed! The meditation is a super-neat way to relax and feel good!

I.W., Newark, NJ

HIGHLY EFFECTIVE

"*Managing Your Stress* is an excellent introduction to basic and practical principles of holistic health. The book is designed to get the reader to actually practice fundamental and highly effective techniques of relaxation and positive health. Highly effective, clearly written, and beautifully designed for the beginning reader."

Robert Frager, Director
California Institute of Transpersonal
Psychology

managing your stress:

how to relax and enjoy

by dr. jerry v. teplitz
with shelly kellman

happiness unlimited publications

To the Spirit of Life within Us All...

First edition © 1977 Jerry V. Teplitz, published by
Japan Publications as *How to Relax and Enjoy...;*

Second edition © 1982 Jerry V. Teplitz, published by
Happiness Unlimited Publications as *Managing Your
Stress: How to Relax and Enjoy;*

Third edition ©*1985* Jerry V. Teplitz;

Reprinted 2002

Photography by Shelly Kellman and Gordon Kramer
Illustrations by Jeanne Ludwig

Published and Distributed by
HAPPINESS UNLIMITED PUBLICATIONS
228 N. Donnawood Drive, Ste 204
Virginia Beach, VA 23452
(757) 431-1317
FAX 757 431-1503
Email: Info@Teplitz.com

ISBN # 0-939372-00-2
Library of Congress Catalog # 81-80175

contents

foreword

Jerry Teplitz is doing important work. He is introducing people to natural, uncomplicated approaches to health maintenance which are extremely valuable in the framework of wholistic health. The wholistic approach to medicine has a very long tradition. It is in keeping with the recorded history of medicine, of Hippocrates, Paracelsus, Maimonides. It recognizes the tremendous advances of present-day medical science, but insists on incorporating them, when appropriate, into an overall understanding and approach to the patient as a total human being, resisting the blandishments and enticements of "modern" medicine to treat the patient merely in terms of a specific disease, focusing on the "pill for every ill" approach.

Wholistic medicine recognizes that a patient is at the moment of presentation to the doctor the sum total of all his life activities—his thoughts, his actions, his desires, his nutrition, his environment. Thus a total cure involves not just an alleviation of the symptoms, but also helping the individual to re-assess his life, to recognize that illness comes about because of a straying from the path of nature. It requires the recognition that the cure lies in his own hands, that he must take responsibility for the mistakes of his own existence, of which his illness is a sign.

He must recognize that some of his activites have divorced him from nature, have alienated him from his true path in life and that it is by finding this path, by once again focusing on his true goal, that he will be cured. He must be helped to understand that the true goal of life is not what we are led to believe—material worth, evanescent pleasure, the pursuit of power—but a complete unfoldment and evolution of one's being, so that when one leaves the corporeal life there has been a progression, an evolution, an advancement, of his total being, which is ultimately of benefit to those with whom he comes in contact. And this concept of personal responsibility has been thoughtfully and carefully presented in this book.

I can heartily recommend this book to you, just as I do to my own patients and students. It is an extremely well-written, concise and comprehensive compilation of some of the most important work in many fields of natural approaches to health. You will learn more than new techniques of self help. You will, and I know this is Jerry's basic purpose, derive a new understanding of the utmost importance of an overall philosophy of positive health and positive living. The basic philosophy that he imparts is his most important contribution.

John Diamond, M.D.
Valley Cottage, New York

Dr. Diamond is the author of BK: Behavioral Kinesiology, *and* Your Body Doesn't Lie; *Director of the Institute of Behavioral Kinesiology; and Past President of the International Academy of Preventive Medicine.*

acknowledgments

We'd like to say THANK YOU and give a great big collective hug to ...
... those people and groups without whom this book would
not have been possible, namely:

> Swami Kriyananda and the Temple of Kriya Yoga
> Belinda Lange Sweet
> Jerry Spiegel and the Lakeview Educational Association
> Happiness Unlimited
> Gordon Seth Kramer
> Maurice ("Uncle Mouse") Webster
> Our parents
> God

AND

... to those who donated time, talent, artistic skills, advice, information
or resources which made the production of this book a lot easier,
namely:

> Justin Pomeroy, for the chapter on Herbs
> Jeanne Ludwig
> Linda Hollar
> Sharon Glass
> Karl Kristoff and Studio K
> Lisa Boynton
> Jon Ludwig
> Patty Baker
> Marcella Ruble–Rook
> Al Gaspar
> JoAnne Canyon–Heller
> John Everest
> Jonathan Phillips
> Pat Yeghissian
> Linda Dovey
> Debbie Morkas
> Carol D. Sigel
> Bob Sandidge, Geoffrey Hulin, and New Orient Media

AND

... to those entities which unwittingly played a part in this work:
All the businesses, associations, and universities to which Jerry has
presented the "How to Relax" program
The Mid–Day Live Show in New York City

introduction

This is a very practical book. You can begin new ways of relaxing almost from the first page. The techniques in this book are easy, effective and quick–to–learn. You can do them by yourself, with a friend, in a group.

I'm the kind of person who always looks for the shortest, simplest way to anything. The exercises in this book are designed to give you the greatest benefits with the least amount of effort or change in your routine.

Most of the material in this book has been field tested many times. For several years, I have been teaching seminars on meditation, yoga, shiatsu and nutrition at colleges and universities, at conferences, and on television shows throughout the country. Several thousand people have experienced the methods in this book, and their response has been remarkable. Almost every single person has thought the programs to be very beneficial. This consistent positive response was one of the things that encouraged me to write this book.

Before I began teaching, I was a practicing attorney. In originally exploring these areas of relaxation, I did it with a trained lawyer's skepticism. While I was intrigued, I thought much of it was gimmicky or just not true. By trying them out for myself, I discovered the tremendous validity and worth of these techniques.

I give this book to you the reader, not just to read, but for you to try out and experience. You will almost immediately notice differences taking place in your level of relaxation. It's fine to be skeptical, but be curious, too.

This book is written as a beginner-level introduction to the various subjects presented. Each chapter is complete and can be done by itself to teach you how to relax. We have included a bibliography for those who would like to pursue these methods further.

If one method of relaxation does not appeal to you, don't close the book and walk away, just turn to another section. There is a technique which will fit just about anyone. You can compare this book to a department store—if you don't find something in housewares, you might find it in hardware.

A unique section of this book is the one on shiatsu. Shiatsu is a Japanese finger pressure technique that is similar to acupuncture. This section includes treatments for the everyday health problems which keep you from relaxing—for example, it's hard to relax when your nose is stuffed up.

The nutrition section of this book is the one section from which you won't see changes instantly; however, by following the advice outlined, you will notice the changes in you and your life within a few weeks.

For me, the fulfilling part of teaching these techniques comes when I meet someone I've taught who says, "You know, I'm amazed. I tried the shiatsu headache treatment on myself and on my friends, and *it works.*"

"I've been meditating regularly and it's incredible, all the changes that have happened to me. I won't miss meditating for anything."

Just by following the simple instructions in this book, you too can both change and take control of your life. While external events and activities will continue to happen, it's actually your internal self that decides your reaction to these external stimuli. For example, two good friends go to see the same movie. Afterwards one says, "Best movie I've ever seen," and the other says, "I didn't really like it." The external event was the same, but both had different internal reactions.

By knowing how to relax, how to energize, how to get rid of headaches or sore throats you'll begin to consciously select how you react to a given situation. If some occurrence makes you tenses, you'll be able to do a breathing exercise. If you feel tired and dragged out, you'll be able to meditate. If you can't fall asleep, you'll be able to do the progressive relaxation exercise.

The "Body Talk" section *must* be tried to be believed. Everything around us has an effect on us. This section will generate a tremendous amount of excitement when you experience the techniques described.

Knowing that *you* are in control is something many people have forgotten. We have been so flooded by product advertisements for this ill or that discomfort that we've forgotten that we are our own best doctors. This lack of control is best illustrated by the fact that about 80% of the people going to doctors are complaining of psychosomatic illnesses—illnesses caused by tension, anxiety, and feelings of an inability to cope.

This book or any section of this book will begin to give you back your rightful power and control over your mind, body and spirit.

Happy relaxing!

breathing

In Hatha Yoga, there is an area called pranayama, meaning breath. In Yoga, breath is viewed as the main life force. This makes sense when one realizes that we can do without food and water for long periods of time, but we can only do for a very short period (3 to 6 minutes) without breathing.

PRANAYAMA IS ALSO A WAY TO RELAX TOTALLY AND COMPLETELY. Have you ever stopped to notice your breathing when you're scared or startled? It would be short and shallow. Any time you feel fear or tension, you can change that feeling simply by changing your breath rate to very long deep breaths.

I have used breathing exercises when scheduled to appear in court in my role as an attorney. To relieve tension before approaching the judge, I would do a breathing exercise. In a minute or two, I'd be calm and prepared to face the courtroom battle.

deep breathing

1. Sit upright, spine straight but not straining.
2. Close your eyes. (If you're in a situation where this would be uncomfortable, you can keep them open.)

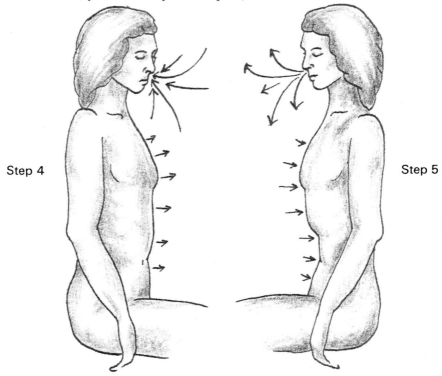

Step 4

Step 5

3. Exhale forcefully all the air in your lungs.

4. Inhale through the nose to a slow count of eight, filling first your stomach, 1 . . . 2 . . . 3 . . . 4 . . . let it expand—then your chest . . . 5 . . . 6 . . . 7 . . . and finally your shoulder blade region . . . 8.

5. Exhale through the nose to a slow count of eight, emptying first your shoulder blades, 1 . . . 2 . . . then the chest . . . 3 . . . 4 . . . 5 . . . and finally the stomach . . . 6 . . . 7 . . . 8. Imagine you are a balloon deflating slowly through a pinhole.

6. Repeat this process at least 2 more times.

7. Sit quietly with eyes closed for a minute or two. Feel how your body is relaxing.

The deep breathing exercise is easy to do any time and any place— on a bus, in a train, in a cafeteria, before a business meeting or taking an exam. For housewives, it is a refreshing addition to morning breaks. It's also good for reducing tension and sharpening your concentration for games like bridge, backgammon and chess. Some athletes habitually do deep breathing and alternate breathing between breaks in the action.

alternate breathing

1. Close your eyes. Sit upright, spine straight but not straining.

2. Press your left nostril closed with your right ring finger and little finger.

Steps 1–2–3   Steps 4–5–6

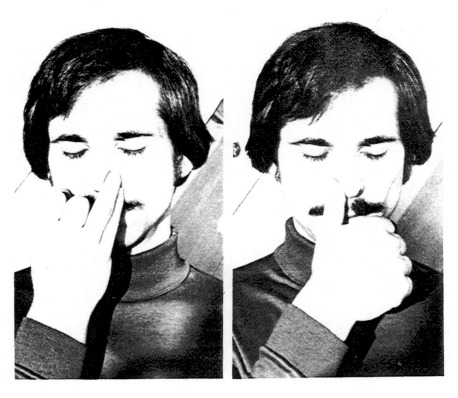

3. Inhale slowly (so you can barely feel your breath coming in) through your right nostril.

4. Release your left nostril. Use your thumb to close off your right nostril.

5. Now exhale slowly through your left nostril.

6. Keep your fingers in position. Inhale very slowly through your left nostril.

7. Close off your left nostril with your ring finger and little finger; release your thumb from your right nostril.

8. Now exhale slowly through your right nostril.

9. Continue doing this for at least 3 to 5 rounds.

10. Sit quietly with your eyes closed and your hands in your lap for a few minutes.

cooling breath

The cooling breath is excellent to use in hot weather. As you take the first breath, you will feel a cool sensation in your mouth. After repeating it 6 to 15 times, you will feel the coolness spreading through your entire body. This exercise will also help reduce fevers.

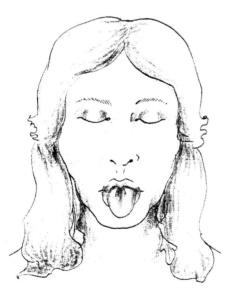

1. Stick your tongue out, with the edges curled up. Don't strain, but stick it out all the way.

2. Inhale air through the mouth, along the center of the tongue, and make a sucking sound. "Sssstthh . . . "

3. When you have a full abdomen of air, swallow.

4. Exhale gently through your nostrils.

5. Repeat 6 to 15 times. Relax and enjoy the cooling sensations.

(Note: Some people cannot curl their tongues properly to do this exercise.)

It might look funny, but it works!

shiatsu

Shiatsu is a pressure point massage technique that's been around for thousands of years. It was formalized in the 1930's by Tokujiro Namikoshi, who founded the Nippon Shiatsu School in Japan.

Shiatsu probably came about when ancient people noticed that we naturally tend to rub a part of the body that is hurting. They also noted the effectiveness of the Chinese technique of acupuncture, which inserts needles into specific body points to promote healing. These principles were combined into a form now called shiatsu, literally "finger pressure."

It can be used to treat many different kinds of pain and illnesses, including: headaches; sore throats and strep throats; sinus colds; migraine headaches; eyestrain; hangovers; backaches; and menstrual pain. These are the treatments in this chapter. Some of the treatments are also great for general relaxation and massage. Several excellent books covering treatments for other problems are listed in the Bibliography.

There are several theories as to why shiatsu works:

1) It increases the flow of blood to the area pressed. The blood carries off wastes from all the cells and brings fresh oxygen, nutrients, hormones, antibodies, and white blood cells to the area.

2) Like acupuncture, shiatsu pressure stimulates the nerve endings and meridians (energy pathways) of the body so that the body will heal itself.

3) In physics there's a principle that every action has an equal and opposite reaction. When you press on a point, then release it, the muscles and blood vessels stretch, expand and relax.

4) When there's pain or tension in muscles, shiatsu relaxes and loosens them—not only at the point pressed, but in the surrounding area. This is akin to a pebble making ripples on a lake. The pebble dropped in one spot makes ripples over a large surface of the water. Unlike the lake, however, our muscles need to be pressed on several points, with repetition, before relaxation comes about.

5) Endorphins, natural pain suppressants secreted in the brain, may be stimulated by shiatsu pressure.

If shiatsu is done properly, pain will disappear or be greatly reduced. This is true even for injuries, such as sprains, and certain infections, like strep throat. We're not suggesting shiatsu as a replacement for seeing a doctor. The treatments in this section are aimed at conditions for which people do not usually seek medical help right away. Rather, the person will reach for some aspirin, a cold tablet, or a pain reliever. Shiatsu is both safer and more effective than any of these drugs. You ingest no chemicals, and the benefits are immediate. If you try shiatsu several times during a day, and feel no relief, then you know you should see a doctor.

An example of shiatsu's effectiveness: I once taught 300 skeptical convention—goers at one time how to do shiatsu on each other for headaches (it works for hangovers, too). They had never heard of it before. At the beginning, I asked, "How many people in here have a headache?" About 30 raised their hands. After I had taught the treatment and they'd done it on each other, I asked, "How many of you still have a headache?" Not one hand went up.

Correct shiatsu pressure is described as a cross between pleasure and pain. You should exert a good, hard steady pressure on each point. Use your thumbs as much as possible. The biggest mistake most people make is not pressing hard enough.

When treating another person use the person's "ouch reflex" as a pressure guide. Tell the person to say "ouch" *immediately* if he or she feels pain. Then let go immediately and press on the next point. Interestingly, a person may feel pain at one point, and one inch away feel no pain at all, even though the pressure is the same.

So, work with the same intensity on each point and let the person you're working on judge when the pressure is too hard. When a person does say "ouch", note mentally the location of that point. Then, on the second time through the treatment, when you come to the location of the "ouch" point, begin by pressing it very gently. Slowly build the pressure up. You'll be pressing for longer than usual, but it's a building pressure rather than a steady one. Surprisingly, you may be able to build more pressure than the first time around, without causing pain.

Another way to experience the kind of pressure you should be using is to place your thumb on a bathroom scale and lean on it until it registers 15 to 20 pounds (30 to 40 with both thumbs).

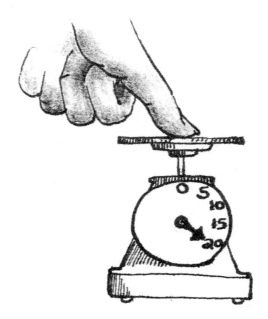

You can do shiatsu on others or on yourself. Like breathing and meditation, it's a handy relaxation tool to carry with you, requiring no special equipment and very little time. For example, the headache cure can be effectively performed in two minutes.

When working on yourself, it may be hard to get a good strong pressure with your thumb on some points. For instance, at the top of your head. When that occurs, put your middle finger on top of your index fingernail and press as shown in diagram A. Or try pressing with the flat of your index finger, supported by your thumb, as in diagram B. *Don't use your knuckle*; just the flat, outside part of the finger.

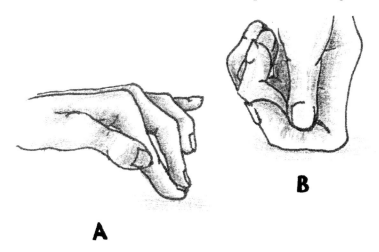

A **B**

These alternate ways of pressing are also useful when you've been doing a lot of shiatsu on other people, to give your thumbs a rest.

When doing a treatment, go through all the points at least twice, even three times if the person still feels pain or discomfort. On yourself, do one treatment more than you'd do on another person, since you're exerting a little less pressure. After three or four times through the points, it's best to wait an hour or so before doing another, just to let the body respond. Shiatsu can be done with complete safety, over and over again.

Follow the diagrams to learn the shiatsu points, but don't worry about pressing each point exactly. The body has a sympathetic and parasympathetic area surrounding each nerve ending. By pressing in the vicinity of the nerve ending, you are stimulating that nerve ending to transmit the healing message to the proper body part. This is why

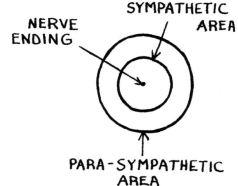

shiatsu points don't have to be "hit" as accurately as acupuncture points, in which the needle must be inserted into exact spots.

Unless otherwise noted, shiatsu instructions in this book are written for the person who is "treating" or working on another person. Occasionally there will be parenthetical statements about what to do differently when working on yourself.

Instructions on your position and which hand to use when treating are written for right-handed people. Left-handed persons can simply reverse the side they stand on and the hand they use, if that's more comfortable. When only one hand is involved, you'll want to press with your stronger hand.

headaches and hangovers

A remarkable 2-minute cure, also great for overall relaxation. This treatment can help chronic headache sufferers by reducing the frequency and severity of their headaches.

The treatment works on hangovers because a hangover is caused by constriction of the blood vessels. When alcohol enters the body, the blood vessels open wider. Then, when the alcohol is gone, the vessels react by tightening up, constricting circulation so much that it's painful. The more you've had to drink, the more violently your blood vessels will react.

Shiatsu opens up the blood vessels, restoring circulation and relieving pain quickly. It's much safer and more effective than the traditional morning-after drink, which doesn't get the body back to normal.

Steps 1–2

Press each point 3 seconds.

1. The person should be seated upright, glasses off, eyes closed, in a comfortable position.

2. Stand on the left side of the person. Support the forehead with your left hand. (No support needed when working on yourself.) With the fleshy part of your right thumb—the ball of the thumb—press at the hairline, in the center of the forehead. Move backwards one inch and press again.

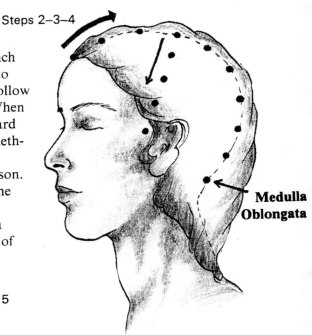

Medulla Oblongata

3. Continue pressing points about an inch apart in a straight line, from the hairline to the hollow at the base of the skull. The hollow is the medulla oblongata. Press it also. (When working on yourself, if these points are hard to reach, remember to use the alternate methods shown on page 17.)

4. Move slightly to the front of the person. Position your thumbs at the very top of the head, the highest point. Press with your thumbs, going down inch by inch on both sides, simultaneously, to the front middle of the ears.

Step 5

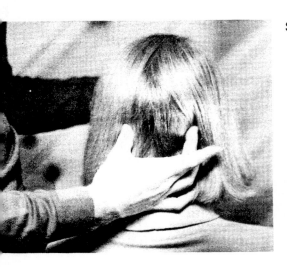

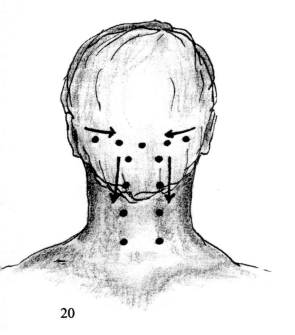

5. Stand to the person's left again. Now you'll be using your right thumb and middle finger, working at the back of the head. (On yourself, use both thumbs.) Find the middle of each ear. From there, go straight in toward the medulla, 1½–2 inches on each side. There you'll find a pair of lumps, little nodes. Press them simultaneously with thumb and middle finger.

Move half the distance in towards the medulla on each side. Press. Then place your thumb on the medulla and press.

6. Come down the neck ½ inch from the medulla. Place thumb and middle finger on both sides of the spinal column, about an inch apart. (On yourself, use both thumbs.) Don't press *on* the spinal column; press right next to it on both sides.

Press 3 or 4 pairs of points, depending on how long the neck is. Just go straight down; points are an inch apart. Stop at the shoulders.

7. Repeat entire process to make one treatment. If the pain has not disappeared, go through the points a third time.

sinus colds

This treatment works when the front of the face feels clogged up, with pressure around the eyes, cheeks, etc. Twice through the points is a complete treatment. After this, ask the person how he/she feels. Most people will be able to breathe again by then. If there's still pressure or congestion, do the points a third time. The person will feel the cold breaking up and draining. If discomfort persists, wait an hour or two and keep repeating the process as needed.

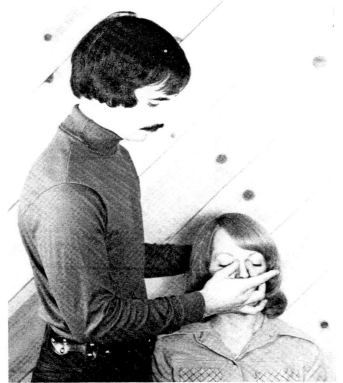

Step 1

Press each point 3 seconds.
Have the person close his/her eyes.

1. Stand on the person's right. Support the back of the head with your left hand. (No support needed on yourself.) With your right thumb and middle finger, pinch in at the bridge of the nose, pressing the fingers towards each other.

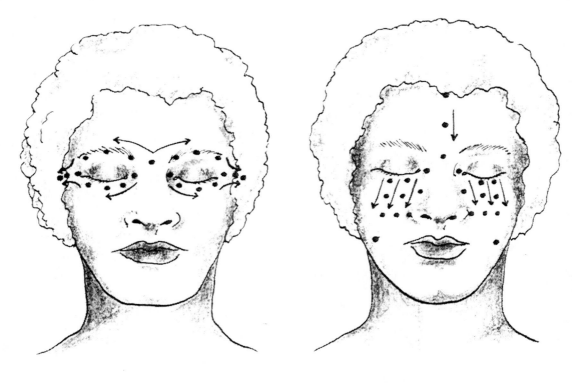

Steps 1–2–3   Steps 4–5–6–7–8

2. Follow the lower eye bone, pressing directly on the bone, skipping an inch between points. Do both eyes at the same time, using your thumb and middle finger, until you get to the outer corners of the eyes.

Using both thumbs, press just behind the outer corners of the eyes, pressing your thumbs inward, towards each other. Continue moving straight back by inches—only one or two points—until you are next to the ears.

. 3. Press in, with your thumb, towards the back of the head, at the point between the eyebrows. With thumb and middle finger, press points *on* the eyebrows, skipping an inch at a time, to the outer corners of the eyes. Switch to both thumbs and press points from the outer corners of the eyes back to the ears, as in step 2.

4. Press with your thumb at the center of the hairline. Press a point halfway down from hairline to eyebrow bone. Then press directly on the eyebrow bone, just above the nose.

5. Pinch in at the bridge of the nose, pressing thumb and middle finger inward towards each other. Then go down half the distance to the nostril openings and press towards the back of the head. The next point is immediately beside the nostril openings; press toward the back of the head.

For steps 6 and 7, continue using the thumb and middle finger of the right hand, simultaneously, on both sides of the face.

6. Return to the lower eye bones, just below the eye sockets, only half an inch outward from the bridge of the nose. Press towards the back of the head. Then drop straight down, halfway to the nostril openings and press; then go down till you're even with the nostril openings and press.

7. Back to the eye bones. This time start about an inch outward from the bridge of the nose. Press the same 3-point sequence as in step 6.

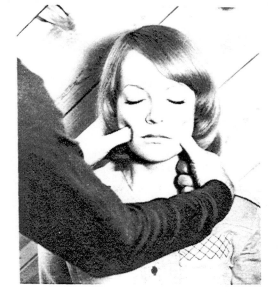

Step 8

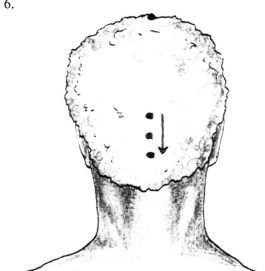

Steps 9–10

8. Find the cheek bones and drop down into the hollows below. Press both sides with your thumbs right in the hollows, pressing them inward, towards each other.

9. Find the crown (top) of the head and press.

10. Move to the person's other side. Support the forehead with your left hand. (Not necessary when treating yourself.) Find the medulla oblongata. This is the hollow at the base of the skull, just above the neck. Move directly up the head 2 inches. Press. Go back down 1 inch and press. Go down one more inch to the medulla, and press it.

Twice through all the steps is one treatment. You may go through them again to bring additional relief.

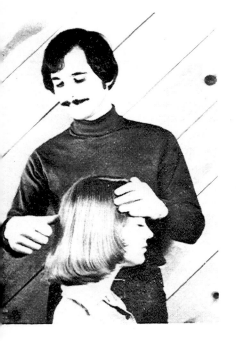

Step 10

23

eye strain

Too much reading or television-watching can make your eyes hurt. Here is a treatment that you can do in about 1 minute to relieve tension, strain or fatigue in the eyes.

Press each point 3 seconds. The eyes should be closed.

1–4. Follow instructions 1–4 and accompanying illustrations for the Sinus Cold Treatment, page 21.

5. Move to the person's left. Now you'll be working at the back of the person's head, using your right thumb and middle finger. (On yourself, use both thumbs.) Find the middle of each ear. From there, go straight in 1½–2 inches on each side, toward the medulla. (This is the hollow at the base of the skull.) You'll find a pair of lumps, little nodes. Press them simultaneously with thumb and middle finger.

Move inwards half the distance to the medulla on each side. Press. Then place your thumb on the medulla and press.

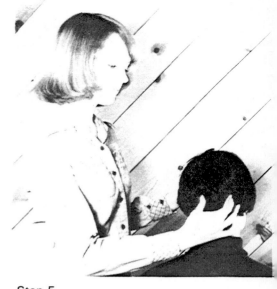

Step 5

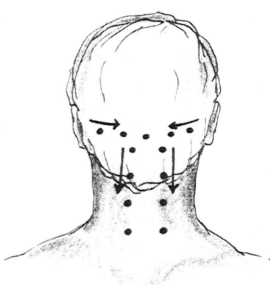

Steps 5–6

6. Come down the neck ½ inch from the medulla. Place thumb and middle finger on both sides of the spinal column, about an inch apart. (On yourself, use both thumbs.) Don't press *on* the spinal column; press right next to it on both sides.

Press 3 to 5 pairs of points, depending on how long the neck is. Just go straight down; points are an inch apart. Stop at the shoulders.

7. Repeat entire process at least once.

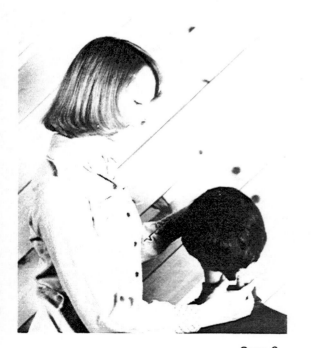

Step 6

lower back treatment

Yes, you can get rid of your own backaches! This treatment will get rid of or greatly relieve lower back pain, strain and fatigue. You can do it sitting up, laying down or even standing.

These instructions are written for you to use on yourself. Before doing this on someone else, read step 1 of "Better Than a Massage" page 38.

Press from 3 to 7 seconds at each point.
1. Begin at the fifth lumbar vertebra. To find it, divide the back in half, horizontally, and drop down 2 inches from the center line. Don't press directly on the spine. Press on both sides of the spine simultaneously, using your thumbs.
2. Move down alongside the spine, pressing points an inch apart, until you've pressed beside the tailbone.

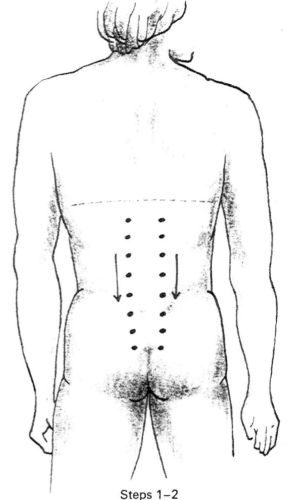

Steps 1–2

Step 1

3. Find the place where the spine and the hipbone meet. Pressing both sides simultaneously with your thumbs, follow the hipbone outwards for four pairs of equally spaced points.

Step 3

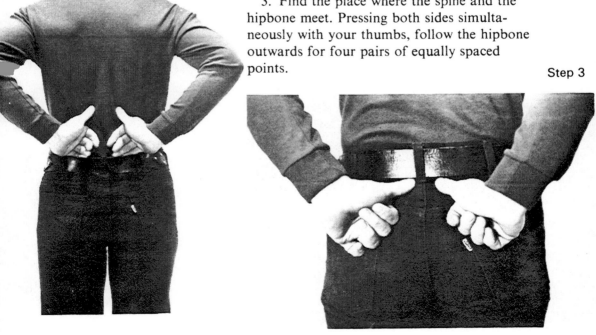

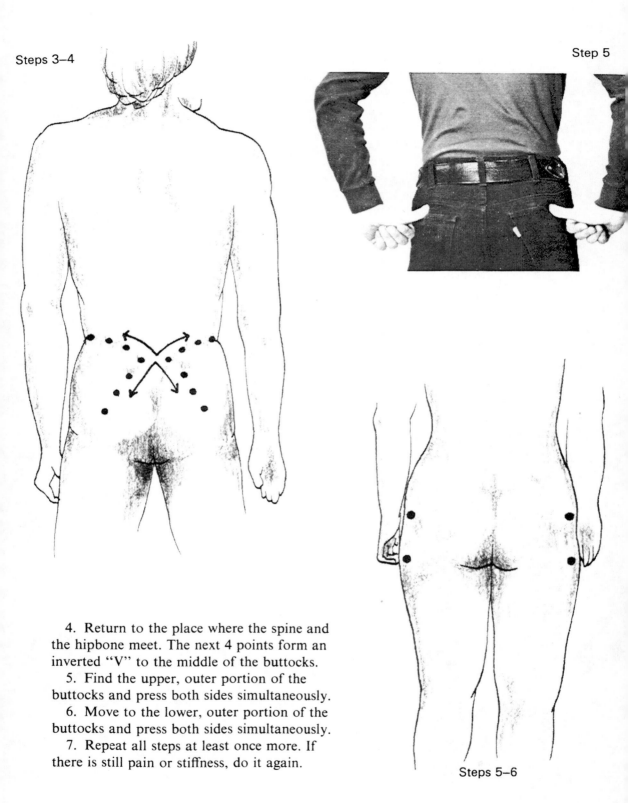

Steps 3–4

Step 5

Steps 5–6

4. Return to the place where the spine and the hipbone meet. The next 4 points form an inverted "V" to the middle of the buttocks.

5. Find the upper, outer portion of the buttocks and press both sides simultaneously.

6. Move to the lower, outer portion of the buttocks and press both sides simultaneously.

7. Repeat all steps at least once more. If there is still pain or stiffness, do it again.

migraine headaches

Anyone who has had a migraine headache or has been around a migraine victim knows the pain and complete helplessness of the sufferer. Shiatsu offers almost instant relief from this problem.

I've done the shiatsu migraine treatment with amazing success on a number of people who suffered from chronic migraines. One person I was called to work on had collapsed from the pain. She needed to be carried into the bedroom. I worked on her for about 10 minutes. Twenty minutes later, she was downstairs cooking dinner.

Another time, I was at a convention and treated a delegate right in the middle of the luncheon banquet. The head of his delegation had approached me, saying that this man had been walking around all day with a headache, and that he was shouting and physically hitting others. When the man came to my table, I asked him if he had a migraine. He said "Yes", so I did the migraine treatment. In a few minutes his migraine was gone.

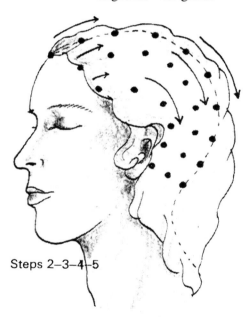

Steps 2–3–4–5

Press each point 3 seconds.

1. The person should sit upright, with glasses off and eyes closed.

2. Stand on the left side of the person. Support the forehead with your left hand. (No support needed when working on yourself.) With the fleshy part of your right thumb press at the hairline, in the center of the forehead.

3. Move back one inch and press again. Continue pressing points about an inch apart in a straight line, from the hairline to the hollow at the base of the skull. The hollow is called the medulla oblongata. Press it, also. (When working on yourself, if these points are hard to reach, remember to use the alternate methods for applying pressure shown on page 17.)

4. Find the center of the hairline again and drop down one inch on each side, towards the temples. With both thumbs, press backwards along the sides of the head, keeping parallel to the center line of the head. Stop when you are next to the medulla.

Step 4

Step 5

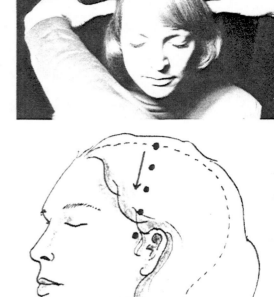

5. Return to the center of the hairline and drop down two inches on each side towards the temple. Again follow an imaginary line backwards along both sides of the head, skipping an inch between points, until you are in line with the medulla. (If the person has a large head, drop down a third inch from the center line and follow the same sequence.)

6. Move slightly towards the front of the person. Position your thumbs at the very top of the head, the highest point. Press with your thumbs, going down inch by inch on both sides simultaneously, to the front middle of the ears.

7. Stand to the person's left again. Now you'll be using your right thumb and middle finger, working at the back of the head. (On yourself, use both thumbs.) Find the middle of each ear. From there, go straight in towards the medulla, 1½–2 inches on each side. There you'll find a pair of lumps, little nodes. Press them simultaneously with thumb and middle finger.

Move half the distance in towards the medulla on each side. Press. Then place your thumb on the medulla and press.

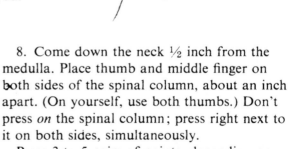

Step 6

8. Come down the neck ½ inch from the medulla. Place thumb and middle finger on both sides of the spinal column, about an inch apart. (On yourself, use both thumbs.) Don't press *on* the spinal column; press right next to it on both sides, simultaneously.

Press 3 to 5 pairs of points, depending on how long the neck is. Just go straight down; points are an inch apart. Stop at the shoulders.

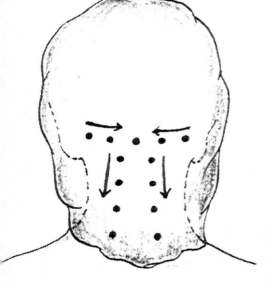

Steps 7–8

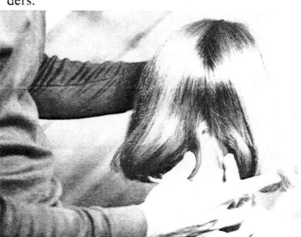

Step 7

9. Now stand on the person's right. Support the back of the head with your left hand. (No support needed on yourself.) With your right thumb and middle finger, pinch in at the bridge of the nose. Press fingers towards each other.

10. Follow the lower eye bone, pressing directly on the bone, skipping an inch between points. Do both eyes at the same time, using your thumb and middle finger, until you get to the outer corners of the eyes.

Using both thumbs, press just behind the outer corners of the eyes, pressing your thumbs inward, towards each other. Continue moving straight back by inches—only one or two points—until you are next to the ears.

11. At the point between the eyebrows, press in, towards the back of the head, with your right thumb. With the thumb and middle finger, follow the eyebrows, skipping an inch at a time, to the outer corners of the eyes. Switch to both thumbs and press points from the outer corners of the eyes back to the ears —only one or two points—until you reach the ears.

Steps 9–10–11

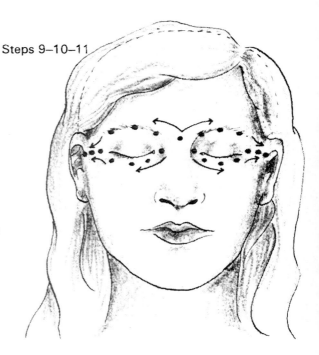

Step 11

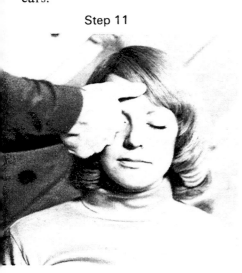

12. Do this entire process at least twice. Then ask the person how she or he feels. If the pain is greatly relieved, but not gone, repeat the process a third time. If the person says that the pain is now localized, just work directly on and around the pain area. Press the same points on the opposite side of the head, even if there is no pain there. You continue to work with a migraine victim until the pain is gone.

menstrual pain

Yes, there *is* something you can do about menstrual pain—your own or someone else's. This treatment brings relief, without drugs. You can do the treatment on yourself, or have someone else do it for you. The cramps will disappear. If they return a few hours later, just repeat the treatment.

Press each point 3–5 seconds.

1. Have the person lie face down. Position yourself on her left. Press all points with the thumbs, keeping arms straight and elbows locked.

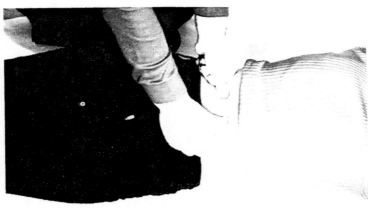

Step 2

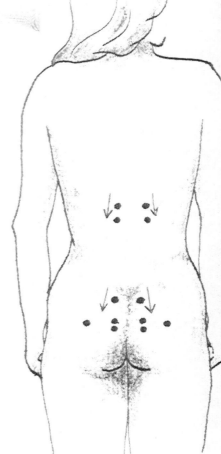

Steps 2–3–4–5

2. **Find the outer ends of the lowest rib. Move straight in towards the spinal column. From this point on the spine, move your fingers up about 2 inches towards the head. This is approximately the first lumbar vertebra. Press right next to the spine (not *on* it) simultaneously on both sides. Next, move your fingers back down the spine until they are in line with the lowest rib. Press.**

3. Find where the hipbone and spine meet. Move down one inch and press next to the spine.

4. Find the tailbone (the very bottom of the spine.) Move up one inch and press along both sides of the spine. Move down 1/4 of an inch and press.

5. From that point, move your fingers outward about 2 inches. This point should feel

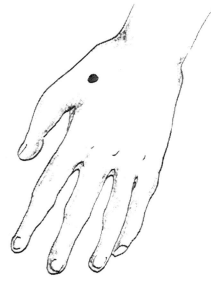

more fleshy. If it still feels bony, move outward a little more. Press on both sides.

6. On the back of the left hand, press the point between the thumb and index finger.

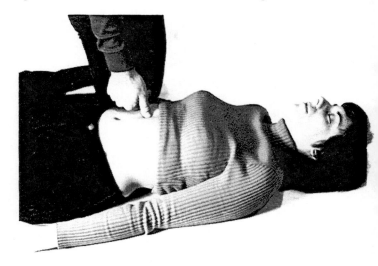

7. Have the person lie on her back. Find the navel and move up about 3–4 inches to a point midway between the navel and the diaphragm. Press.

Steps 7–8–9–10–11

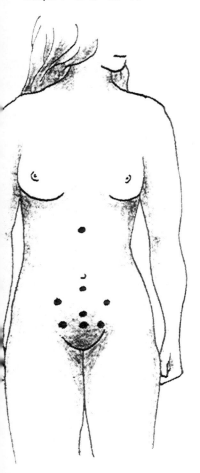

8. From the navel, drop down 1 inch and press.

9. From the navel, drop down 3 inches and press.

10. From the navel, drop down 2 inches and then move outward 2 inches on each side. Press both sides simultaneously.

11. From the navel, drop down 4 inches and then move outward 1 inch. Press both sides. Next, move back inward 1 inch and press.

12. On both legs, find the knee cap. Move upward 2 inches, then over 1 inch toward the insides of the thighs. Press.

13. Find the middle of the calf muscle (the back position). Move 1 inch inward on the inner side of the muscles, and press both legs.

14. Find the inner anklebone on both legs and move up 3 inches on the inside of each leg. Press.

15. Find the inner anklebone, and press the point behind it on each leg.

Repeat the entire treatment.

Step 7

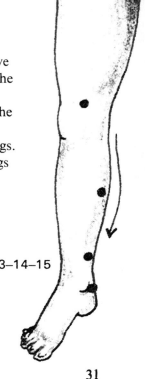

Steps 12–13–14–15

the body's natural purification plant

We can understand how shiatsu works on sore throats, colds and other infections by understanding the lymphatic system—our natural internal filtering and purifying plant.

The lymphatic system is a network of vessels, larger intersection points (the lymph nodes), and the fluid (lymph) that flows through the vessels. Although it is located almost parallel to the circulatory system, it functions quite differently. The system's three main jobs:

1) Returns protein that leaks out of body cells (a normal occurence) to the blood vessels, which return it to the cells.

2) Absorbs and breaks down harmful bacteria, toxins, foreign matter and certain waste particles into harmless substances. The breaking-down is done by specialized cells found mainly in the lymph nodes. (Imagine them as waste treatment centers.)

3) Manufactures antibodies to protect the body against infection, and fight off infection once it's there. Specialized cells along the walls of the lymphatic vessels do this; the lymph carries the antibodies to the bloodstream.

How fast all of these functions are performed depends on how fast the lymph goes through the vessels. The lymph circulates around the body . . . collecting the wastes and foreign matter from tissues, carrying these things through the filtering cells, and delivering "clean" products and antibodies into the bloodstream via the capillaries.

Unlike the circulatory system with its heart, however, the lymphatic system has no pumping mechanism. What keeps it going? Two things— one is the fluid pressure between all the body cells, and the other is simple muscle movement. It is the latter that interests us in shiatsu.

Every time a muscle stretches or contracts anywhere in the body, it squeezes the lymphatic vessels, causing the lymph to flow faster throughout the whole body. The more muscle activity, the faster flows the lymph.

The shiatsu treatments for sore throats and colds put direct pressure on the lymphatic vessels, lymph nodes and muscles. We can see that the hard shiatsu pressure speeds up the lymphatic flow. This means:

More protein is returned to all the body cells.

More invading bacteria, toxins and waste particles are cleaned out and broken down.

Antibodies get into the bloodstream faster.

You may have noticed that your sore throats are sometimes accompanied by "swollen glands"—tender, painful lumps on your neck beneath the hinges of your jaw. These are actually swollen lymph nodes, swollen because they've got a lot more work to do when there's an infection nearby. Shiatsu pressure on the area helps this system perform better, helping the body to heal itself naturally.

sore throat, streptococcic throat, laryngitis, "smoker's throat"

A complete treatment (once through entire sequence) will either cure a sore throat or greatly relieve the pain. On strep throat, the treatment must be done several times a day, up to once an hour or so if needed. For smoker's throat, this treatment will reduce the closed-up feeling and help drain out phlegm.

Laryngitis may require up to one treatment an hour before improvement is felt. However, I once did this treatment on a film company executive with an acute case of laryngitis. By the end of the 3-minute process, she was shocked to find herself speaking normally and painlessly.

The treatment is also beneficial before giving a speech or singing.

You don't necessarily press more lightly on a throat than on a head; let the person's "ouch" be your guide. (For further explanation, see page 17.)

Step 1

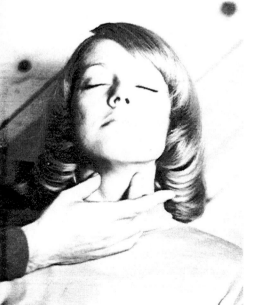

Press each point 3 seconds.

1. Stand on the right of the person you're working on. Support the back of the head with your left hand. (Not necessary on yourself.) The center of the throat, from chin to chest, is protected by a tube of cartilage, soft bony material. Using your right hand, gently feel the throat to find where the cartilage is. Move upward to where the throat and jaw connect, and press with thumb and middle finger along both sides of the cartilage. Press straight back, towards the back of the neck.

When doing the treatment on a person more than 45 years old, press on one side of the throat at a time.

Drop down an inch, following the cartilage and pressing right next to it—not directly *on* it. The third and fourth points are called "coughing points." Widen the distance between your thumb and finger *slightly*, and

33

press. If the person coughs, move your fingers apart a bit more.

The fifth point is the hollow of the breastbone. Use your thumb to press straight *down* on the bone—towards the floor.

2. Repeat step 1 two more times.

3. Stand in front of the person. Put your middle and index fingers together, on each hand. You're going to do a circular massage down both sides of the throat. Start just behind the jaw and circle down to the sides of the Adam's apple—but not onto it. Circle down with a good, hard pressure all the way. Do that 4 times.

Steps 1–2   Step 3

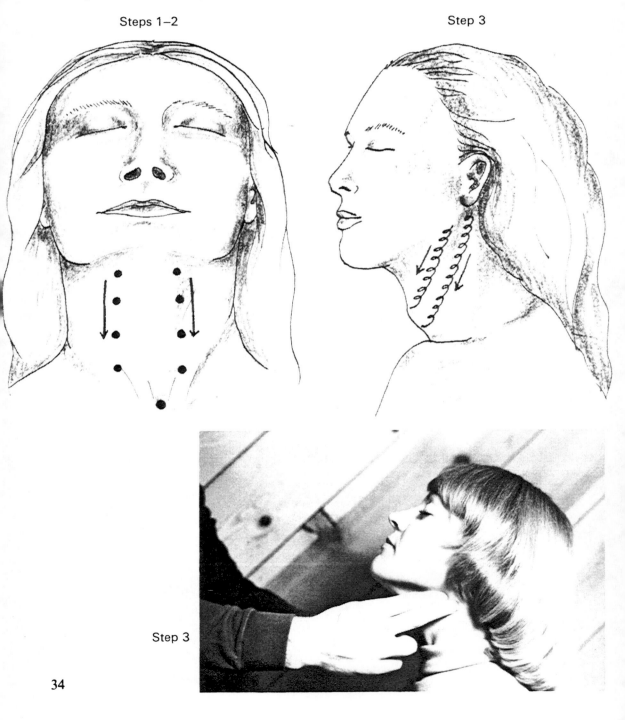

Step 3

34

A second circular massage starts at the bottom of the ears and ends just below the Adam's apple, alongside the cartilage. Do that 4 times.

4. Stand to the person's left. You're going to work on the back of the head, using your right thumb and middle finger. (On yourself, use both thumbs.) Find the middle of each ear. From there, go straight in towards the medulla oblongata, the hollow at the base of the skull.

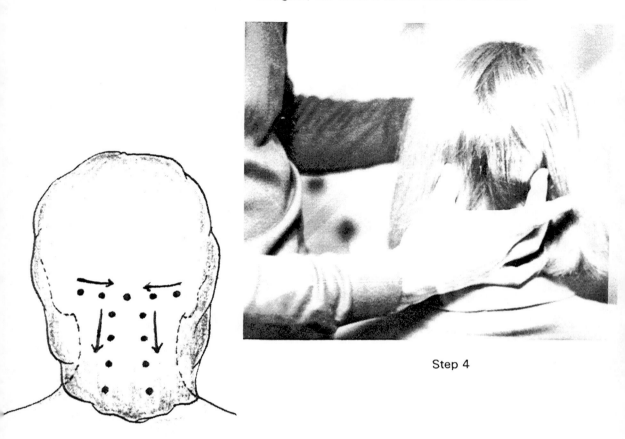

Step 4

Steps 4–5

About 1½–2 inches inward from each ear, there's a lump, a little node. Press these.

Move inward half the remaining distance to the medulla on each side, and press. Then place your thumb on the medulla and press.

5. Come down the neck ½ inch from the medulla. Place thumb and middle finger on both sides of the spinal column, about an inch apart. (On yourself, use both thumbs.) Don't press *on* the spinal column; press right next to it on both sides simultaneously.

Press 3 to 5 pairs of points, depending on how long the neck is. Go straight down, skipping an inch between points. Stop at the shoulders.

6. Repeat steps 4 and 5.

35

stiff neck & shoulders

One of the most common, most annoying complaints I hear from people in my workshops is that they are bothered by stiff necks and shoulders. The type of lifestyle and work behavior that is common now, particularly long periods of sitting or standing in one place, causes us to lean over and crunch up our shoulders. This position causes stiffness.

About a year ago, I had occasion to sleep overnight in a train, in a chair that moved only into a semi-reclining position. I woke up in the morning with a *very* stiff neck. I did the following treatment on myself, and gained immediate relief. (Instructions are written as if doing the treatment on a partner.)

Press each point 3 seconds.

1. The person being treated should sit upright, glasses off, eyes closed, in a comfortable position.

2. Stand on the left side of the person. Support the forehead with your left hand.

3. You'll be using your right thumb and middle finger, working at the back of the head. (When treating yourself, use both thumbs.) First find the midpoint of each ear, just behind the ears. From there, move thumb and finger towards each other, on a straight line towards the *medulla* (hollow at the base of the skull, just above the neck). About 1½ - 2 inches behind the ears, you'll find a pair of lumps—little nodes.

Press these nodes simultaneously with thumb and middle finger. Move half the distance inward towards the medulla on each side, and press again. Then place your thumb on the medulla and press.

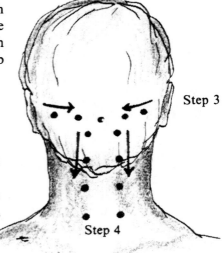

Step 3

4. Move down the neck ½ inch from the medulla. Place thumb and middle finger on both sides of the spinal column, about 1 inch apart. (On yourself, use both thumbs.) Don't press directly *on* the spine; press right next to it on both sides.

Press 3 or 4 pairs of points, depending on how long the neck is. Just go straight down, an inch at a time. Stop at the shoulders.

Step 4

5. Go back to ½ inch below the medulla. This time place thumb and middle finger on both sides of the spine, about *two* inches apart. (On yourself, use both thumbs.) This time, press your thumb and finger (or both thumbs) *towards* each other.

Press 3 or 4 pairs of points, going down the neck as in Step 4. Stop at the shoulders.

6. Stand directly behind the person. Draw an imaginary line along the top of each shoulder.

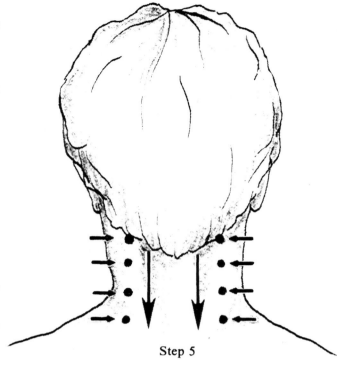

Step 5

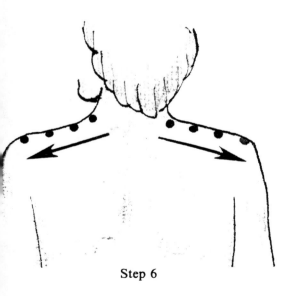

Step 6

Using your thumbs, press pairs of points starting at the base of the neck and moving outward an inch at a time, to the top of the arms.

(On yourself, treat one shoulder at a time. Place your middle finger on top of your index fingernail (see diagram A, p. 17). Bring your hand across your body as if saluting the flag, to the base of your neck. Use the combined pressure of your two fingers to press the points going outward to your arm. Then use your other arm in the same way to treat the shoulder opposite it.)

7. Repeat the entire process 2 or 3 times. (On yourself, repeat 3 or 4 times.)

"better than a massage" (full back treatment)

You can't do this treatment on yourself because you can't reach all the points. Besides being a great massage technique, this treatment is excellent for promoting general health and well-being, as it stimulates the entire body.

This massage is unusual in that it is effective even if the person is fully clothed. However, feel free to use full or partial nudity, oils, candles, or whatever you prefer for a sensuous massage. None of these trimmings is necessary, but all are fine if you like.

1. Have the person lie face down on a firm surface. You are on the left side. Have the person close his/her eyes. I suggest staying on the left side of the person you're working on. If you straddle the person, don't sit on the buttocks, since this can cause a strain on the person's back.

2. Do a circular massage between the shoulder blades with the palm of your right hand. Rub with a firm pressure, using fairly rapid movement, and continue for about 30 seconds. Remember to stay between the shoulder blades (not the neck). This part of the back is called the web area, and it contains many nerve endings, so you are loosening a much larger area than you're actually rubbing.

3. To get an idea of where you'll be pressing, use your thumbs to trace down the spinal column from the top of the shoulder blades to the coccyx, or tailbone. Throughout this treatment, keep your arms straight with the elbows locked. Lean your body weight onto your arms while pressing each point.

Never press directly on the spinal column; always on both sides of it.

Press each point 3–7 seconds.

4. Place your thumbs alongside the spine, about an inch apart, at the top of the shoulder blades. Work down from the shoulder blades, skipping an inch between points, until you get to the tailbone. Use the heel of your hand to apply pressure on the tailbone.

Steps 3–4

Step 4

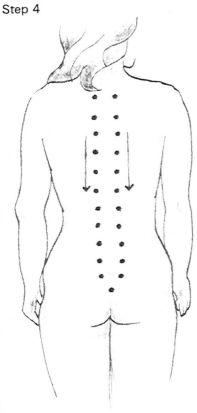

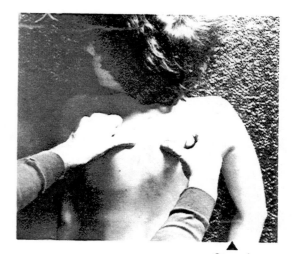

▲ Step 4.
First Points

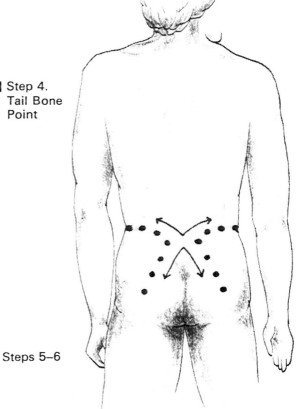

◄ Step 4.
Tail Bone
Point

Steps 5–6

. Find the hips, and trace along the hip-
e to the spine. Work outward along the
bone, towards the sides of the body,
sing 4 evenly spaced points on each side.
ss on both sides simultaneously with your
mbs.

. Return to the place where the spine and
bone meet. The next 4 point pairs form
inverted "V" which ends in the middle of
buttocks. Press with both thumbs simul-
eously.

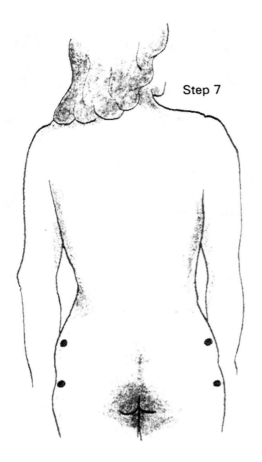

Step 7

7. Find the upper outer area of the buttocks and press on both sides. Then move to the lower outer part of the buttocks, and press.

8. Steps 4 to 7 are done at least twice and possibly three times for one complete treatment or massage.

9. To conclude the massage, you "chop wood," as if the person's back was a log. Turn your hand sideways, so the fleshy outside of your hand is towards the person's back. Keep your hands slightly cupped and relaxed. Chop rapidly up one side of the person's back and down the other—*don't* chop directly on top of the spine. Move from your elbows. You can chop pretty hard, and you should hear a good, solid thumping sound. Do this for a minute or so.

10. Tell the person to remain still until he/she feels ready to get up.

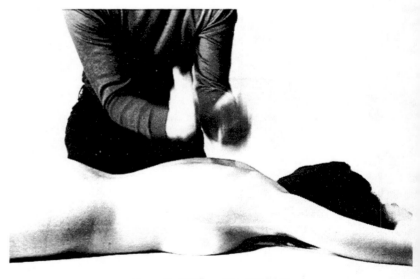

Step 9. "Chopping Wood"

hatha yoga

Hatha Yoga is a way of relaxing and stretching your body, which in turn relaxes your mind. As you do these postures (exercises) you'll find yourself becoming more aware of your body and how it feels.

As you may know, there are many Yogas. There is a yoga of work (karma), a yoga of love (bakti), a yoga of philosophy (jnana) and others. Some of the teachings and practices are at least 5,000 years old.

Hatha Yoga is the physical yoga, which uses the physical postures or "Asnas" as a means of achieving union with the universe, or a god–consciousness. Since yoga is *not* a religion, it is totally compatible with whatever religious philosophy an individual might be following.

One of the key elements of yoga is that it's *non-competitive*. You are not competing against an expert, a friend, or even against yourself. This means you don't push yourself further than you can go; don't try to withstand any pain. You're just going up to the pain point—the uncomfortable point—and moving back from it so that you stay comfortable.

Yoga is done very slowly, so that you flow into a position, hold it, and flow out of it. Let your body regulate its own stretches. Some days you stretch more than other days. Stretching in the morning is always harder than later in the day, but morning yoga helps you start the day feeling limber and energetic.

I recommend doing yoga every morning for 2 weeks. Then, for a pleasant surprise, try some in the afternoon. Since your muscles are looser in the afternoon, you'll be amazed at the progress you've made.

While you can do any of the postures right now, just to relax, the recommendation for general health is to start with one posture a day for 5 minutes. At the end of a week, you've put in only 35 minutes and have stretched your body 7 different ways. Of course, it's fine to start out with more if you want to.

Many people conceive of yoga as a series of difficult contortions that take years of study and practice. That's not necessarily so. It may take quite awhile to reach advanced yoga postures that look truly impossible. But it all starts with some very simple movements. The ones I present here are easy, effective and can be done by anyone. The point is always to *stay comfortable*. If a few inches is a comfortable stretch, that's fine.

Before I started doing yoga, I had what is commonly known as a "bad back." It was constantly annoying, and once every couple of months, my back would go "out," causing me to stand crookedly, limp awkwardly, and feel extreme pain in any position except lying down. At the age of 24, I had lived with this for most of my life. When I first tried yoga 10 years ago, I couldn't stretch more than a few inches in some directions. But look at me now! And I haven't had a back problem since.

A few other points to keep in mind:

Always do yoga slowly (butterfly and back roll are the only exceptions in this book). *The slower the better*. Imagine it as a drifting, floating gentle movement into each posture . . . rather than a bouncing or jerking. During the writing of this book, my collaborator came to me with a complaint. "This umbrella posture (p. 55) is too hard. I can't get anywhere with it! You'll have to change it," she said. I had her try it, and saw that she was moving quickly, as if doing calisthenics. I told her to try it again, much more slowly. Doing the posture at about ⅓ her previous speed, she found it easy.

Although some yoga movements may resemble calisthenic movements, there's really no similarity. The slowness, avoidance of strain, and breathing in yoga make it a completely different process, and a different experience for the person doing it.

Proper breathing is a very important part of yoga, and breathing instructions are included with each posture. The right breathing makes the postures easier, and allows you to achieve a great feeling of lightness and relaxation. Except where otherwise noted, breathing is done through the nose.

Once you have learned the postures, you will enjoy doing yoga even more with *eyes closed*.

Before starting yoga, read the Total Relaxation Pose (next section).

Don't be alarmed . . . however:

If you have a heart problem, you can do yoga with your doctor's permission. When you exercise, just make sure to tense your muscles very gently.

For women, if it is within 3 days before your menstrual period, avoid doing the leg raises and back rolls.

People with lung problems should do the postures very gently.

total relaxation pose

The benefits of yoga are many-faceted. The movements are good for stretching and toning the muscles, gently exercising the heart and lungs, adding to gracefulness, bodily control and general health. However, the *relaxation* in yoga comes *after* the movements . . . during the total relaxation pose, when the muscles relax in response to the stretching and tightening that has just taken place.

Do the total relaxation pose after completing each yoga posture, and for five minutes at the end of your yoga session.

Even if you do no other yoga, the total relaxation pose for 5 minutes a day will help you feel more relaxed and rested.

1. Lie down on your back with arms alongside your body, but slightly away from your sides. Turn palms upward. Let your fingers curl so that thumb and index finger form a circle. Your legs should be slightly apart

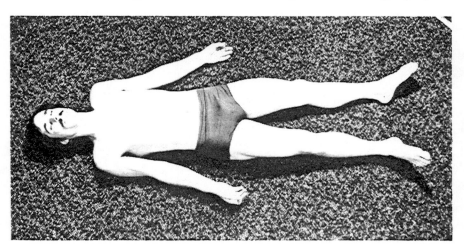

with toes turned outward.

2. The important part of this pose is your breathing. Breathe deeply into your abdomen, filling up your entire stomach. Inhale slowly and exhale slowly through the nostrils. Continue this deep breathing the entire time you are in the position. There is no holding the breath, just slowly in and out.

3. When resting between other postures, don't go on to the next posture until your heart and breath rate have returned to normal. Again, at the end of a yoga session, or when doing this by itself, continue for 5 minutes.

4. When you are finished, turn the palms down and raise your body up slowly.

neck exercises

Ours is a society of stiff necks. People spend a lot of time with their necks in one position while working, reading, studying, or watching television. This exercise will eliminate all soreness and tension.

The entire sequence of movements takes about five minutes, once you know it. It's a good thing to do in the morning, say in the shower or bathtub.

Many people tend naturally to stretch their necks in these ways when they feel tense, but they often do it in a fast, jerky manner. This yanks the muscles and is not as relaxing as stretching slowly, gently and smoothly. A fast movement may *feel* more effective at first, but that's because the muscles are protesting and holding back. You can actually pull a muscle that way. If you keep up a slow pace from beginning to end, you'll feel how much more relaxed your muscles are.

1. Sit up, feet flat on the floor. If you wear glasses, take them off. Close your eyes.

2. Drop your chin toward your chest to a slow count of 1 . . . 2 . . . 3. Hold for a second or two.

3. Begin to raise your head upright, 1 . . . 2 . . . 3, and continue backwards without stopping, 4 . . . 5 . . . 6, back as far as your head will go without strain. Hold.

Step 2   Step 3

4. Slowly repeat steps 2 and 3 two more times. Then bring your head upright again.

5.A. Slowly drop your left ear toward your left shoulder, 1 ... 2 ... 3, without raising your shoulders. Hold for a second or two. Your head doesn't have to touch your shoulder; if stretching two inches is all that feels right, that's fine.

5.B. Raise your head upright, 1 ... 2 ... 3, and lower it, 4 ... 5 ... 6 towards your right shoulder. Hold. Then raise your head upright and repeat these sideways stretches twice more. Finally, re-center your head upright.

Step 5-B

Step 6

6. Without moving your back or shoulders, turn your head as if looking over your left shoulder, 1 . . . 2 . . . 3 . . . 4. Go as far as you comfortably can, and hold it.

Turn slowly to the right to a count of 8 and look over your right shoulder. Hold it. Repeat these movements, rotating from side to side twice more. Don't let your shoulders hunch up. You'll be feeling the muscles that connect the neck and shoulders stretching and relaxing.

7. Center head upright. Drop your chin to your chest and circle your head to the left to a slow count of eight. 1 . . . 2 . . . 3 . . . 4, you're half way around, 5 . . . 6 . . . 7 . . . 8, it's a complete circle. Let your head *roll* as much as possible. Do 2 more of these slow circles to the left.

Step 7

Now circle to the right, 1 . . . 2 . . . 3 . . . 4 . . . 5 . . . 6 . . . 7 . . . 8. Do it 2 more times.

8. Center your head upright. Don't open your eyes. Rub your *palms* together, building up a lot of friction, a lot of heat. Rub them fast, till they feel very hot. With eyes still closed, place your palms at the back of your neck and inhale through your nose, deeply and slowly. Feel the life-giving energy, the vitality, the heat coming into your neck through your palms. Exhale through your mouth. Feel any tension, any strain, any remaining fatigue going out from your neck through your mouth. Continue inhaling and exhaling at least 4 times.

9. Relax. Drop your hands. Open your eyes.

eye exercises

Our eyes are always being bombarded by things to look at—
billboards, signs, addresses, movies, TV, and the things we read for
work, study or pleasure. Our eyes are so active that we may develop
eyestrain without knowing it. This makes us feel tired, headachy or
unable to concentrate, when it's really just our eyes that need a rest.

Practice these exercises two or three times with your eyes open, so
you know how it *feels* when you are moving your eyes in the right directions. After you know the movements, the entire sequence should be
done without opening the eyes.
You will find it more relaxing
that way.

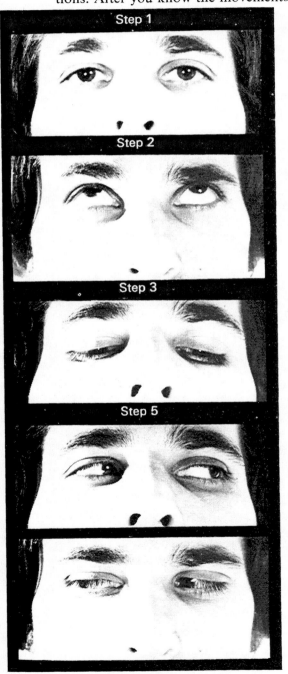

1. Sitting upright, focus on a point directly
in front of you as your center point (when
you do this with your eyes closed, it will be
an imaginary point).

2. Without moving your head, raise your
eyes up towards the ceiling, as high as they
can go without straining. Only your eyes
move, nothing else. Hold for a few seconds.

3. Move your eyes towards the floor, as far
as they can go. Hold for a few seconds.

4. Repeat the upward and downward
movements twice more. Always hold for
a second or two at the farthest points.
Bring eyes back to center and rest for a few
moments.

5. Move your eyes to the left as far as you
can. Hold. Then go back to the right as far
as you can, and hold. Repeat this twice more.
Bring eyes back to the center and rest for a
few moments.

Step 6

6. Move eyes diagonally up to the left. Hold. Then diagonally down to the right. Hold. Do this twice more. Center and rest.

7. Move eyes diagonally up to the right—hold—then diagonally down to the left—hold. Repeat twice more. Return to the center point and rest.

8. Now make complete circles slowly with your eyes. Don't rush through them, but don't stop and hold at any point. Begin by moving your eyes left, then down, then to the right, then up, then left again. A smooth flow. Circle to the left twice more. Return to the center point and rest a few seconds.

9. Now circle to the right, down, to the left, up and to the right again. Continue through two more circles to the right. Back to the center and rest.

Step 10

10. Keeping your eyes closed, rub your *palms* together, building up a lot of friction, a lot of heat. Rub them fast. When palms feel very hot, place them over your eyes—just cupping your eyes, not pressing on them. Inhale very deeply and slowly. Feel energy, vitality and heat coming from your palms into your eyes. Exhale rapidly through your mouth, and feel yourself exhaling any remaining strain or fatigue that may be in your eyes. Continue inhaling and exhaling at least 3 or 4 times.

11. Relax. (Ah . . .)

This exercise feels much better with eyes closed than open. If it's hard for you to believe that your eyes are moving properly when closed, try this. Close them and gently place your fingertips on the eyelids. Now move your eyes to either side. Hold. You may be surprised to find that you've done the movement correctly.

butterfly

The butterfly stretches the inner thigh and relaxes the legs. It's a great warm–up and unwinding exercise for before and after sports. Try it to limber up for swimming, gymnastics, tennis, bike riding, climbing and hiking.

If your legs are stiff from some activity, or from standing on your feet all day, this simple movement will relax them. When you stand, your legs have to work against gravity, sending waste-carrying blood "uphill" to the heart. The butterfly makes this easier by stretching and strengthening the leg muscles, increasing circulation.

This posture is also recommended as a warm-up for the back roll (next posture).

1. Sitting on the floor, bring the soles of your feet toether, as close to your body as is comfortable, so that you look like you have wings.

2. Hold onto your toes with your hands, keep your back straight, and flap your legs up and down as if you were flying. Your feet should stay on the floor, your knees bounce.
FLAP QUICKLY—this is one yoga posture that is not done slowly. As you are flapping, put a slight pulling pressure on your feet, pulling them towards your body. Flap for at least 30 seconds.

back roll

This warm-up exercise for yoga will stretch the spinal column and relax the back muscles. Most people don't exercise their backs much, although they do put strain on their backs, sitting in offices and the like. So this exercise is good for almost anyone.

Step 1

1. Sit on the floor with knees drawn up to your chest and feet flat on the floor. Knees can be apart. Clasp your forearms just under your knees.

The proper breathing in this exercise is to exhale while rolling backwards, inhale while rolling forwards.

Step 2

2. Roll backwards as far as you can, stretching your legs out as you go. Try to have your toes touch the floor behind your head. After you have gone back that far, roll forward to a sitting position.

If you can't roll back till your toes touch the floor, just rock back and forth on your spine.

You don't have to do this exercise slowly, and you don't hold at any one point. Just back and forth, 6 to 15 times.

leg raises

Excellent for strengthening the legs and stomach, and warming up the body for other postures.

Step 1

1. Lie on your back, hands at your sides with palms down.
2. Raise your left leg . . . first 6 inches . . . then 12 inches . . . then straight up to form a 90 degree angle to the floor. Do this as slowly as you can manage (but remember, no pain). Always keep your leg straight, even if this means you can't raise it as far as you'd like.

Step 2

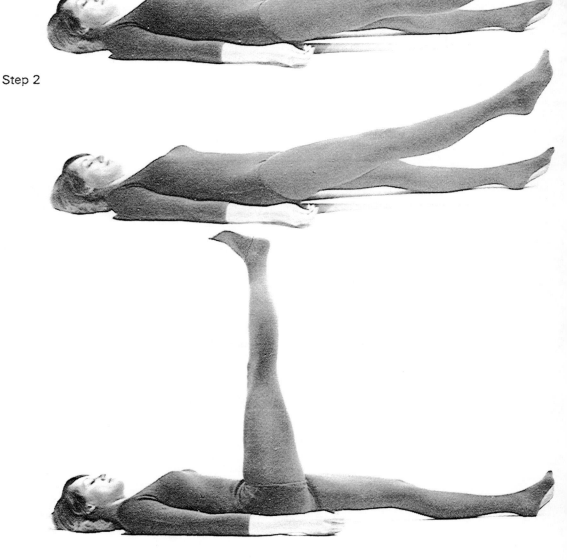

3. Lower slowly to the floor.

4. Raise and lower your left leg 3 times. Repeat with your right leg . . . 6 inches . . . 12 inches . . . then straight up. Lower slowly each time.

5. Raise both legs together . . . 6 inches off the floor . . . 12 inches . . . then straight up. (This will be harder, at first, than raising legs separately. The most important thing is to keep legs straight.) Lower slowly back down. Do this 3 times.

6. Do the Total Relaxation Pose (p.43).

Step 5

the cat

The cat stretches the spine, relieves neck strain, and helps firm the stomach muscles.

1. Take a position on your hands and knees as if you were a cat. Hands about shoulder width apart.

2. Inhale deeply and slowly through your nose, filling your stomach and chest.

3. While exhaling, lower your head and bring your chin to your chest, and curve your back upwards towards the ceiling. Hold that pose, with empty lungs.

4. Begin to inhale, meanwhile turning your fingers inward, so that they are facing each other. Raise your head up. Lower your chest towards the floor between your fingertips, bending your elbows. Go down as far as is comfortable and hold that position with lungs full. Hold for several seconds.

Step 1

Steps 3 and 5

Step 4. Lowering

5. Begin to exhale, turning your fingers outward again. Bring your chin to your chest while you straighten your arms and curve your back upward. Hold with empty lungs for several seconds.

6. Do these movements 4 to 6 times, at a slow pace. Remember to stay comfortable.

7. Do the Total Relaxation Pose (p. 43).

Step 4. Fully Lowered

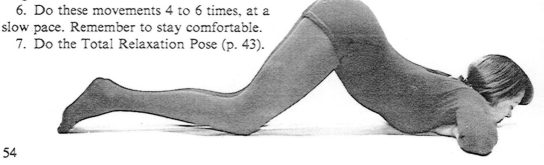

umbrella

Excellent for the stomach, as well as upper and lower back.

Step 2. Fully Lowered

Step 2. Lowering

Step 1

1. Place your feet a little less than shoulder width apart. Place your arms behind your back and intertwine your fingers. Pull your shoulders back. Inhale.

2. As you exhale, bend from the waist towards your left leg, keeping your back arched, head up. While bending, raise your arms up towards the ceiling, raising them up behind you as far as you can comfortably go. Hold for a few seconds at your furthest point. While bending, keep your back arched and head up as long as possible, then try to touch your forehead to your knee. (If you can't do this, don't worry.)

3. While inhaling . . . raise head, arch back and lower arms. Meanwhile, slowly return to the standing position.

4. Repeat the same bending and raising movements toward your right leg.

Each time you've gone down and up once, you can take a few breaths to rest before continuing. Do this exercise 3 times in each direction.

5. Finish with the Total Relaxation Pose (p. 43).

posterior stretch

This posture may feel difficult at first, since most of us in this society are sitting-oriented. Unless we're active hikers, ballet dancers or tennis players, we don't get much stretching of the hamstring muscles (back of the leg). When you begin doing this posture, don't be surprised if you can move only a few inches. (That was about the furthest I could move before I began doing yoga regularly . . . remember the pictures on page 42.) By the end of two weeks, you'll be amazed at how far you can stretch.

Steps 1–2

1. Sit on the floor, legs straight out in front of you, feet together. Your weight should be on the front portion of your buttocks, almost on your thighs. To get there, imagine that you are walking, taking 3 steps forward. Go through that motion. Sit erect.

2. As you inhale, slowly raise your arms along the sides of your body, stretching towards the ceiling. With arms up as far as they can go, hold the stretch for a second or two.

Step 3. Lowering

3. Keeping your back arched and head up, lower your upper body towards your legs. Slowly. Always keep legs straight. When you have lowered as far as you can go, grasp onto the part of the legs that is closest to your hands. Hold for 2 or 3 seconds, keeping lungs empty. (If you can touch your chin to your legs and grasp your toes, you are way beyond the beginner stage.)

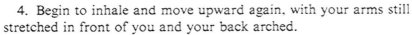

Step 3. Fully Lowered

4. Begin to inhale and move upward again, with your arms still stretched in front of you and your back arched.

5. When you are straight up again, slowly lower your arms to your lap and exhale.

6. Rest until breathing and heartbeat are back to normal before doing this 2 more times. If you like, you can put your hands on the floor by your sides for support while resting.

cobra

The cobra tones and strengthens the back and stomach muscles. It can aid in the prevention of lower back problems and pains.

1. Lie on your stomach, feet together. Place your palms on the floor beside your shoulders, with fingers forward. Your forehead should be on the floor. Inhale.

Step 1

Step 2. Raising

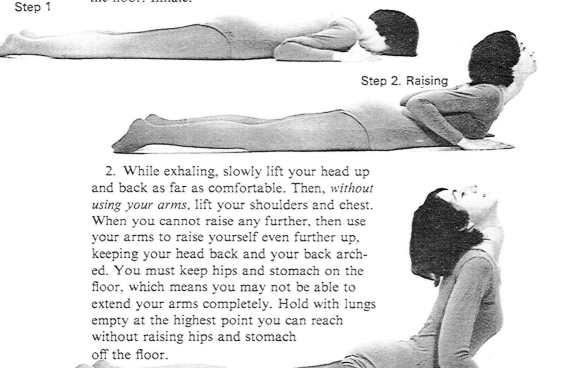

2. While exhaling, slowly lift your head up and back as far as comfortable. Then, *without using your arms*, lift your shoulders and chest. When you cannot raise any further, then use your arms to raise yourself even further up, keeping your head back and your back arched. You must keep hips and stomach on the floor, which means you may not be able to extend your arms completely. Hold with lungs empty at the highest point you can reach without raising hips and stomach off the floor.

Step 2. Fully Raised

Step 4. Resting

3. Begin to inhale. Lower slowly by easing down first onto your stomach . . . then chest . . . then forehead.

4. Bring your hands up to form a pillow under your forehead. Rest until your breathing and heartbeat return to normal. Repeat the exercise twice more.

5. After the third time, return to the Total Relaxation Pose (p. 43).

57

insomnia or general relaxation

progressive relaxation

You can do this exercise lying down or sitting upright. If you do it lying down, you're apt to fall asleep, which makes this exercise good for insomnia or temporary sleep difficulty. If you don't fall asleep after one time, try it a second or third time through.

If you do this exercise sitting up, you'll be totally relaxed.

It's nice to have someone read this to you, at least the first time through. The reader should read slowly and pause a few seconds between steps. You, or someone whose voice you like, can also put this on a cassette tape. Be sure to read slowly, and leave pauses for doing each step.

Step 2

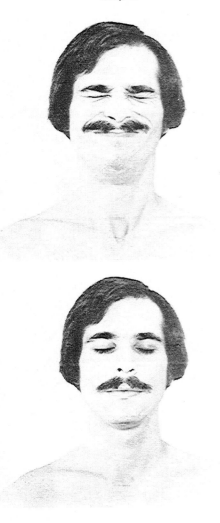

1. If you are lying down, lie on your back with arms alongside your body, but slightly away from your sides. Turn palms upward. Let your fingers curl so that thumb and index finger form a circle. Your legs should be slightly apart with toes turned outward.

If you are sitting up, put your feet flat on the floor and sit with your spine straight but not stiff.

Close your eyes.

2. Tighten your face muscles by squinting your eyes, wrinkling your nose, and tightening all the facial muscles. Keep tightening those muscles . . . tight . . . tight . . . tighter . . . really tense . . . tenser . . . then relax them completely.

3. Inhale very deeply and slowly through your nostrils. Then exhale very deeply and slowly. Feel the tension and strain flowing out of your face.

4. Take your awareness to your neck and shoulders. Tighten them up . . . really tight . . . tighter . . . tense . . . tense . . . tenser . . . then relax them completely.

Step 3

5. Become aware of your arms. Make a fist and tighten all the muscles in your arms. Tense up your hands, palms, forearms, and triceps. Tighten them . . . tighter . . . tighter . . . even tighter . . . then relax. Let your hand and arms go completely limp in your lap or by your sides.

6. Inhale and exhale very deeply and slowly through your nostrils. Feel the tension and strain flowing away.

7. Take your awareness to your chest. Tighten all your chest muscles really tight . . . really tense . . . tighter . . . tenser . . . even tighter . . . then relax completely.

8. Become aware of your stomach and buttocks. Tighten all of the muscles in your stomach and buttocks really tight . . . tight . . . tight . . . tighter . . . even tighter . . . then relax.

9. Inhale very deeply and slowly . . . and exhale very deeply and slowly.

10. Take your awareness to your legs. Stretch them out in front of you. Arch your toes and tighten all the muscles in your legs . . . your thighs, your calves, your feet . . . really tight . . . tighter . . . tense . . . tenser . . . even tenser . . . then relax. Feel your legs sinking into the floor . . . deeper and deeper, as you become more and more relaxed.

11. Inhale and exhale very deeply and slowly.

12. Take your awareness from the very tip of your head to the very bottoms of your feet. Tighten your entire body . . . make a face. . . curl your hands . . . arch your toes . . . tense your arms . . . chest . . . stomach . . . buttocks . . . legs . . . face . . . tighter . . . tighter . . . even tighter . . . then relax completely.

13. Inhale very deeply and slowly through the nostrils . . . exhale very deeply and slowly. Again, inhale and exhale very deeply and slowly.

14. Relax for a few minutes in this position, breathing normally.

Step 12   Step 13

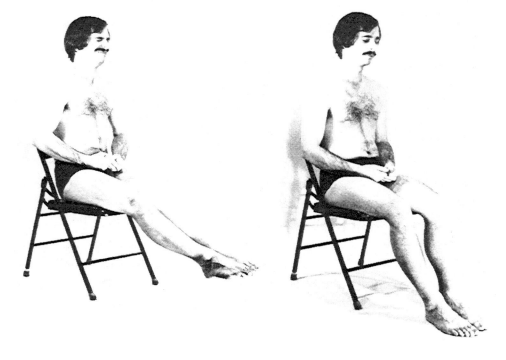

mind and body relaxation

This exercise is excellent for recurring insomnia or temporary sleep difficulties, as well as general relaxation or relief of tensions, anytime.

In this exercise, you will not be moving at all. You will not even be tensing or contracting your muscles. Instead, you will be telling your body to relax, part by part. By thinking relaxation to your muscles, you can actually get them to relax. This has been demonstrated in experiments with biofeedback, in which people learn to control their heart rate, blood pressure and brain-wave activity just by thinking about what they want those functions to do.

Have someone read you through this exercise, at least the first time, so that you can concentrate on relaxing, not on the reading. It should be read slowly, with a 2–3 second pause after each numbered step. Words in parentheses are instructions to the reader and should not be read aloud.

1. Lie down on your back in the position described in step 1 of Progressive Relaxation, page 58. Close your eyes.

Become aware of the top of your head. Silently, tell all the muscles in your head to relax. Say to yourself, over and over:

(Relaxation Message)

"Relax . . . relax . . . you are relaxing . . . you are unwinding . . . letting all tension flow away . . . relax . . . you are letting go of all strain . . . relaxing . . . you are relaxing . . ."

(You can vary the words and add other relaxing words if you wish.)

Visualize your muscles completely relaxing, stretching out into a soft, comfortable position like a cat going to sleep.

2. Take your awareness to your forehead. Tell all the muscles in your forehead to relax. Say to the muscles in your forehead:

(Repeat relaxation message in step 1, above.)

3. Take your awareness to your eyes. Tell all the muscles in your eyes to relax. You are not moving your eyes at all; you are just thinking relaxation to them. Say to the eye muscles:

(Repeat relaxation message.)

Keep visualizing the relaxation taking place. In your mind you can see all the muscles around your eyes relaxing . . . and all tension flowing away.

4. Inhale and exhale through your nostrils, very deeply and slowly.

Fill your entire stomach and chest with the breath before letting it out, slowly.

5. Take your awareness to your neck. Tell all the muscles in your neck to relax. Tell your neck to:

(Repeat relaxation message.)

6. Take your awareness to your shoulders. Tell all your shoulder muscles to relax. Say to your shoulder muscles:

(Repeat relaxation message.)

7. Take your awareness to your triceps, that is, your upper arm. Tell all those muscles to relax.

Take your awareness to your forearms. Tell all those muscles to relax.

Take your awareness to your hands and fingers. Tell all the muscles in your hands and fingers to completely relax. Visualize the relaxation taking place in your arms, as you tell all of those muscles to:

(Repeat relaxation message.)

8. Take your awareness to your fingertips and palms. Feel a tingling sensation in your palms and fingertips. Draw that tingling energy into your body and slowly back to your mind. You're still not moving at all. Bring the energy through your forearms . . . triceps . . . shoulders . . . neck. Place the energy at the base of your skull. Tell it to wait there and you'll come back.

9. Inhale and exhale through your nostrils, very deeply and slowly. Fill your entire stomach and chest with the breath before letting it out, slowly.

10. Now, take your awareness to your chest. Tell all the muscles in your chest to relax. Say to your chest muscles:

(Relaxation Message)

"Relax . . . relax . . . you are relaxing . . . all tension is draining away . . . all tightness is flowing out of you . . . relax . . . relax . . . you are relaxing . . . all tension is melting away . . . you are completely relaxing. . ."

(Reader can add or substitute similar words and phrases.)

11. Take your awareness to your stomach. Tell all of your stomach muscles to relax. Say to them:

(Repeat relaxation message.)

12. Take your awareness to your buttocks. Tell every muscle in your buttocks to relax. Tell them to:

(Repeat relaxation message.)

13. Inhale very slowly and deeply, through your nostrils, filling your stomach and chest. Exhale slowly through your nostrils.

14. Take your awareness to your thighs. Tell all the muscles in your thighs to relax. Take your awareness to your calves. Tell all the muscles in your calves to relax. Take your awareness to your feet and toes. Tell all the muscles in your feet and toes to relax. Visualize all the muscles in your legs relaxing and unwinding, visualize all tension leaving, as you say to every one of your leg muscles:

(Repeat relaxation message.)

15. Take your awareness to the bottoms of your feet. Feel a tingling sensation. Begin to draw that energy into your body, up to your mind. Draw the energy slowly through your ankles . . . calves . . . thighs . . . buttocks. Place that energy at the base of your spine. Then move it slowly up the spine to right below the navel . . . then to the abdomen . . . then the heart . . . then the throat.

Have that energy join with the energy from your arms which you left at the base of your skull. Let all that energy enter your mind and place it at the point between your eyebrows. Hold it there for a few seconds . . . then release all the energy back through your entire body, let it rush out through your arms and legs.

16. When you are finished, just stay still and enjoy the feelings of relaxation.

meditation

Meditation is absolutely amazing. It can totally revitalize your entire system in a very, very short period of time. Research on the physiology of meditation has shown that it slows the heart rate by about 5 beats per minute. Breathing slows down. All the vital signs—blood pressure, muscle tension, etc.—are greatly slowed. Meditation has even *cured* high blood pressure in some patients.[1]

During meditation, your brain produces an abundance of alpha waves, described as a state of relaxed awareness. As a matter of fact, meditation produces a lower rate of body activity than even the deepest part of sleep. This is why 20 minutes of meditation gives you as much deep rest as six to eight hours of sleep.

Most people who meditate regularly find they need less sleep. I used to need nine to ten hours a night, but now with meditation I need only seven hours. Meditating regularly takes just 20 minutes, twice a day. So, you gain time in your day by needing less sleep and by having more energy, which means you can get more done.

Do you wake up in the morning with the world groggy and your eyes fuzzy and an urge to throw the alarm clock out the window? After your morning meditation, you'll be clear-headed and raring to go.

After a day of work, study or play, your early evening meditation will refresh your body and mind. Instead of wanting to crawl into bed and go to sleep, you'll feel wide awake and ready to go again.

Meditation can make life easier for persons whose jobs sometimes require them to do without sleep, such as reporters, firefighters, and computer programmers. If you are working on an all-night project or studying for an exam, meditate once more at midnight. This will enable you to stay awake. When morning comes and your head is spinning, do your regular morning meditation. You'll be alert and ready for the day. (Note: This third meditation should be done only occasionally, not daily.)

Speaking of sleep, many people ask, "What's to keep me from going to sleep while I meditate?" Nothing, but don't worry about it. Your body is saying, "Wow, you are giving me this opportunity to rest and I'm taking it. I'm tired." When you wake up and realize you've been sleeping, don't open your eyes and get up. Instead take an extra five minutes of meditation time; otherwise you may not feel completely refreshed. Sleep is not the purpose of meditation, though. That's why meditation is done sitting or kneeling, not lying down.

Another interesting fact about meditation is that you don't really need quiet and solitude for it. It might feel better in a quiet place, but research indicates this isn't necessary.

One group of scientists tested meditators with instruments that measure certain vital signs, such as heartbeat, brain waves and breath rate. After the meditation the researchers asked, "How did it feel?" Some subjects said, "Great, best meditation I've ever had." Others said it was terrible, they could hardly sit still, they were distracted by the machines, they couldn't concentrate on relaxing. But the readings showed that *all* subjects were at the same deep levels of rest and relaxation. These results indicate that no matter how you feel about your meditation, you're doing fine as long as you sit there and do it for the required time.

This also means that you can meditate in a car, plane, cafeteria or anywhere you need to, and still benefit from it. It may not feel like the best meditation you've ever had, but it's working.

In a *Psychology Today* article titled "Meditation Helps Break the Stress Spiral" (February, 1976), associate editor Daniel Goleman, Ph.D., reviewed half a dozen major studies confirming the benefits of meditation. The researchers were psychology faculty at Harvard, the University of Pennsylvania, Ohio State University and other schools. Among their findings:

* Meditators can withstand *more* life changes with *less* illness than non-meditators.

* Meditation develops the ability to solve life problems, and to cope with feelings of hopelessness and depression.

* Experienced meditators feel more in control of their lives than beginning meditators.

* Meditators report feeling much less anxiety each day than non-meditators.

* Meditators have fewer colds, headaches and sleeping difficulties.

* Meditators react faster to a tension-producing event, both physically and mentally, than non-meditators. After the event is over, meditators relax quickly and easily. Non-meditators stay tense much longer. (Some didn't relax at all during the research time.)

* Meditation trains the capacity to pay attention.

A wide variety of other research has linked meditation with increased intelligence, better memory, improved work performance, greater job satisfaction, higher grades for students, improved relationships with supervisors and co-workers, and faster reaction time.[2] Evidence correlating regular meditation with lowered blood pressure, lowered blood lactate (a substance associated with anxiety), lowered heart and breathing rates, more and deeper alpha brain waves (associated with calmness and feelings of well-being), and dramatic decreases in smoking, liquor consumption, and the use of marijuana, hallucinogenic drugs, and narcotics is reviewed by Harvard Medical School professor Herbert Benson, M.D., in his famed book *The Relaxation Response* (New York: William Morrow & Co., 1975).

Regular meditators consistently report that they are happier, more at ease with themselves, and better able to cope with personal problems than they were in pre-meditation days.

Personally, when I first heard these kinds of statements I said, "Hah! That couldn't be." I was extremely skeptical. Nothing that simple could cause such enormous changes in one's life. However, I also looked at the physiological studies that had been done on meditation, which indicated that at least I might get some energy from it. So I tried it. After I'd been meditating for a while, I asked some close friends if, quite honestly, they had noticed any changes? They told me that I seemed happier, more joyous, and more at ease with myself. It was like hearing a tape recording of what I'd been told would happen. I suggest trying it for at least two or three weeks so you can feel the benefits for yourself.

do's and don'ts

1.) THE KEY TO GETTING ALL THE BENEFITS IS TO MEDITATE REGULARLY TWICE A DAY, 20 MINUTES EACH TIME. In the morning, do it anytime before breakfast. If you don't eat breakfast, do it before you start your day's activities. In the afternoon, do it anytime before dinner.

You can also substitute several shorter meditation periods throughout the day. So long as they total 40 minutes, you'll get the benefits.

2.) GIVE IT A CHANCE TO WORK. During the first two weeks, try staying away from any drugs, medication or alcohol. This will give you a chance to distinguish the changes that are happening.

3.) IF YOU WEAR CONTACT LENSES, REMOVE THEM. Otherwise, you may wind up meditating on the pain in your eyes.

4.) IF YOU FIND YOURSELF THINKING OF OTHER THINGS, DON'T WORRY ABOUT IT. DON'T FIGHT IT. OBSERVE THE THOUGHT, LET IT GO, AND RETURN TO THE MEDITATION TECHNIQUE. Suppose you are meditating and then you start thinking, "Wonder what I'll have for dinner?" Then you become aware that you've been thinking, not meditating. "Oh, no!" You might think. "I blew it!" This is not the right way to handle your thoughts. You shouldn't be angry or upset at yourself.

The right way to handle a thought: You become aware that you've been thinking about what's for dinner. You calmly say to yourself, "Oh, there's a thought." Then you let it go and return to the technique.

Possible Intrusions or Distractions	What to Do:
Worrying Remembering a fight you had with someone Daydreaming about someone you love Unmade decisions Scenes from a movie you saw last night Unexpected strong feelings Things you have to get done	(1) Observe that the thought is there. (2) Let it go, gently. Don't worry about it, or about how it affects your meditation. (3) Return to the technique.

5.) IF YOU HAVE AN ITCH, SCRATCH IT, IMMEDIATELY. If you have to blow your nose, blow it. If your leg falls asleep, move it.

If you don't take care of your physical discomforts, you'll end up meditating on them. It is so much easier to just scratch the itch and let it go.

6.) IF YOU HAVE TO GET UP WHILE MEDITATING—to answer the phone or the door—Do IT. Get up and take care of the interruption, then come back as soon as you can, even if you were almost done, and meditate for another five minutes. While meditating, you've been in a very deep state of physiological rest, and the disturbance brings you too suddenly back to the waking state. It's a slight shock to your system, so you return to meditating for another five minutes in order to come out of it slowly and smoothly.

7.) DON'T MEDITATE JUST BEFORE BEDTIME. It may wake you up!

8.) YOU CAN TIME THE 20-MINUTE PERIOD IN ONE OF TWO WAYS. Either set up your own internal biological clock, the inner sense that wakes you up at 7:30 a.m. even on Saturday and Sunday . . . or have a clock easily in view, so you can open one eye for a brief glance at the time. Don't use an alarm clock; it's as jolting as a phone or doorbell ringing.

I'd advise using a clock or watch each time you meditate since there is a time distortion that usually takes place. The 20 minutes may seem to last forever or to go by in a flash. Both kinds of distortions will continue to occur, no matter how long you've been practicing meditation.

9.) DON'T MEDITATE AFTER EATING. You will wind up meditating on your stomach! A stomach full of food wants to digest, and will divert extra blood to that region. Since meditating reduces your circulation and heart rate, you get two systems working in opposite ways—one wanting to speed up, the other wanting to slow down. The conflict will make you mainly aware of your stomach.

10.) IF YOU DON'T FEEL RELAXED AND ENERGIZED AFTER OPENING YOUR EYES, MEDITATE FOR ANOTHER 5 MINUTES. You may have come out too quickly, or not taken the extra 5 minutes after falling asleep. In that case, another 5 minutes and "Finishing Up" (p. 70) will have your feeling relaxed and energized again.

11.) "HOW DO I KNOW I'M DOING IT RIGHT?" Meditation is a very subjective process. Some meditations you will never want to end, and others you'll feel you hardly want to continue. As I mentioned before, the benefits for you are the same either way. Remember, it works because you do it *regularly*.

and now it's time to start

Read this section all the way through before beginning. Four techniques of meditation are included. If possible, have a friend read two of them to you the first time you meditate. The reader should go through one technique and leave you with it for 10 minutes. Then, he or she should softly read you into another technique and leave you for 10 minutes. You should keep your eyes closed the entire time.

Once you pick a technique, stick to it and don't vary for the first 2 to 3 weeks, just to get a good rapport with the technique. Then you can try others, if you wish. Stick to any technique you try for at least 2 to 3 weeks.

If you are visually oriented, I suggest the Object of Beauty technique; otherwise, try Hong Saw or Watching the Breath. There is also a meditation for couples.

No matter what technique you use, start with the following 2 instructions, and end with the *Finishing Up* instruction at the end of this chapter.

A. Sit against a wall or in a chair, whichever is comfortable. If you're on the floor, cross your legs. In a chair, cross your legs or place your feet flat on the floor. If you are not used to sitting upright, it's good to have your back supported. Otherwise, you'll meditate on the tensions in your back.

If you have glasses on, take them off. If you have a tight belt, loosen it. If your clothing is constricting, loosen it. Do anything you need to feel unconfined and relaxed.

B. Do this exercise to straighten your spine: Raise your arms up over your head and stretch towards the ceiling. Stretch your arms and neck

up . . . get a good stretch. Twist your entire body from the waist, first to the left, hold . . . then to the right, hold. Keep stretching upwards throughout the twists. Do the twists slowly. Come back to the center, stretch up one last time, and lower your arms slowly.

Your back, which was like a winding country road, is now a highway to send messages of relaxation all over your body.

hong saw

1. Keeping your eyes closed, become aware of your breathing. Become aware of your inhalation and exhalation, but don't try to regulate it. Just let your breath do what it wants to do.

2. Now, each time you inhale, you're going to say to yourself, silently, the word "hong." Envision the word entering your head at the point between your eyebrows. (If you can't see the word clearly, it's O.K.)

3. Each time you exhale, you're going to say, silently, to yourself the word "saw," and see the word exiting at the point between your

Step 2   Step 3

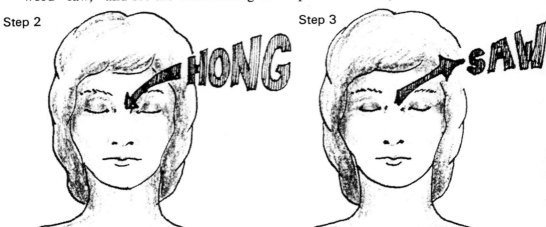

eyebrows.

4. You'll be inhaling and seeing "hong" enter, then exhaling and seeing "saw" exit. Remember, just let it follow your natural breathing. If your breath is shallow, that's fine; if it's deep, that's fine. If it stops, don't worry; it'll start when it wants to. Don't change your breathing deliberately. Just keep doing HONG . . . SAW for 20 minutes.

object of beauty

1. Find an object, sound, color, word, scene . . . something that holds beauty for you.

2. Take that sound, object, color or other beautiful thing and place it at the point between your eyebrows.

3. Examine it there.

4. Gradually, you'll begin to get a feeling of beauty from your object of beauty. Let this feeling fill your entire being, your entire body.

5. Send this feeling of beauty out into the room . . . fill the room with it. Send the feeling out as far as you're comfortable . . . to surround the building . . . the town . . . and the earth. Send it even into the universe.

6. If you lose your feeling of beauty, just return to your object of beauty, and re-examine it between your eyebrows until the feeling returns. Again, extend the feeling of beauty outward.

7. Try and focus on one object only; don't keep changing your object of beauty. Continue this technique for 20 minutes.

watching the breath

1. Close your eyes and begin by becoming aware of your breathing. Don't try and regulate it, just allow the breath to do what it wants to do, at whatever rate it wants to go. Simply be aware of what your breath is doing.

2. On your inhalation, feel the coolness of the air coming in through your nose. Follow this coolness as far back as you can.

3. On your exhalation, follow the warmth of the air from as far back as you can comfortably.

4. Just continue to follow the coolness when you inhale and the warmth when you exhale. Continue for 20 minutes.

dyadic meditation or meditation for couples

1. You do this technique with a partner.
2. Sit opposite each other with knees touching. You can be in two chairs, or cross-legged on the floor.
3. This meditation is done with your eyes open. Begin looking into your partner's left eye with both your eyes. Your partner will be looking with both eyes into your left eye. If you need to blink, that's OK, but try to keep it at a minimum.
4. Do this for 5 to 15 minutes.
5. When the time is up, gently break eye contact and discuss with your partner what you both felt and experienced.

finishing up

After 20 minutes are up, stop doing the technique. Keep your eyes closed. Sit comfortably for 2 minutes, without doing anything. If you feel like moving an arm, leg, neck, etc., just do it gently. After this waiting time, you can open your eyes. Don't rush this part . . . you'll need that 2 minutes to physiologically come from a very deep state of relaxation to a state of wakefulness.

nourish thyself: foods and relaxation

A few years ago, anyone into health foods was automatically labeled a "health nut," an excessive worrier, a hypochondriac. This seems to be changing now as more and more information is coming to light verifying that the normal U.S. diet, often called a "junk food diet," is the cause of much illness and suffering—and that a health food diet is really better for us. A health food diet doesn't necessarily come from a health food store, although certain items are easiest to get there.

Until recently, diet was not stressed as a part of health care and medical treatment. In some medical schools, nutrition is covered in only one course[1]. Thus, doctors haven't been trained to look for nutritional answers to health questions. The only time nutrition has been considered was when a deficiency was gross enough to become a disease, as in scurvy, beriberi, pellagra, and the like.

Meanwhile, the question of what foods, nutrients and combinations we need for optimum health has been all but ignored. The Minimum Daily Requirements once used as guidelines to our vitamin and mineral needs were devised by the Food and Drug Administration as the absolute minimums needed to stave off deficiency diseases. In response to the complaint that MDR's told us nothing about what we needed for good health, the Food and Nutrition Board of the National Research Council developed Recommended Dietary Allowances (RDAs).

how accurate are the rda's?

To answer this question, let's turn to a statement made by Senator William Proxmire in the United States Senate in June, 1974, that is still accurate today:

▶ "There are a dozen or more reasons why the so-called RDA is a capricious, unscientific and illogical standard.

▶ "First and foremost is the unconscionable conflict of interest of those on the Food and Nutrition Board which establishes it. The Board is both the creature of the food industry and heavily financed by the food industry. It is in the narrow economic interest of the industry to establish low official RDA's because the lower the RDA's the more nutritional their food products appear.

▶ "The present Chairman of the Food and Nutrition Board, for example, occupies an academic chair funded by the Mead Johnson Baby Food Company. He appeared at the FDA vitamin hearings not only as an FDA–Government witness but also on behalf of such firms and groups as Mead Johnson and Abbott Laboratories. He was also scheduled to appear on behalf of the Pet Milk Company and Disillation Products. His research was funded to the tune of about $40,000 by the FDA and he had additional government grants of about $90,000 in the year he appeared for the FDA.

▶ "In the 1974 edition of the Food and Nutrition Board's RDA's, most values that were changed were lowered from previous standards . . . .

▶ "With low RDA's the food companies . . . can then print tables on their food packages making their products appear to contain a higher level of nutrients than if higher or optimum levels were established.

▶ "A second reason why the RDA standards are suspect is that they have fluctuated capriciously from year to year both in the nutrients listed and in the Recommended Daily Allowance. For example, in the recommendations by the Board for panthothenic acid, a B-complex vitamin, in the period 1964–1974—it was not on the 1964 list, was listed at 5 mg. on the next list, was not on the third list, was back at 5 mg. on the fourth list, was doubled to 10 mg. on the fifth list, and was removed completely from the latest 1974 edition.

▶ "In the 1968 RDA list, there were 55 changes in value from the 1964 list, varying from 20 to 700 per cent. The latest (1974) list shows similar subjective and unscientific variations.

▶ "Third . . . there is a very considerable body of scientific evidence that the RDA's are ridiculously low. For example: *Folacin*. The RDA for folacin for some categories of individuals has varied by 700 per cent in the last 10 years. The latest pronouncement cut the

RDA for children in half. This has come at the very time the Canadian Government's nutritional survey found that half of all Canadians had moderate deficiency's levels of folacin in their blood . . .

▶ "There is strong evidence that the lack of folacin produces congenital deformities and increases the danger of accidental hemorrhage by five-fold."[2]

Senator Proxmire raises some serious doubts about the absolute reliance many persons place on the government's nutritional standards. There will be further discussion of vitamins and minerals later in this Chapter.

The now-famous study in which mice were found to gain more nutrition from eating cardboard cereal boxes than from the cereals inside points out that we've got a lot to learn about the eating habits we take for granted.[3]

it's not all in the mind

I'll cite two studies that illustrate the profound changes that alterations in diet can bring to a person.

The first was a study of hyperactive children: children who misbehave in class, can't seem to concentrate, have a short attention span, run around nervously, etc. The standard treatment today is psychoactive drugs, ranging from tranquilizers to amphetamines. No one really knows why any of these drugs works or fails to work.

When a group of hyperactive children was removed from the typical American diet—and given *no* drugs—their hyperactivity disappeared. A simple removal of sugar, preservatives, white flour and chemical additives from their diet transformed them into normal, fun-loving children . . . able to pay attention and concentrate. When one child on the diet was given a processed cookie by a friend, the ill effects lasted for 3 days.[4]

The second area involves the use of megavitamin therapy. This is the use of large doses of vitamins to cure certain diseases.

Schizophrenia, a mental illness, was the first area in which mega-vitamin therapy was employed. In 1952, Abram Hoffer, M.D. and Humphrey Osmond, M.R.C.P. found that nearly 75 percent of their schizophrenic patients improved with vitamin treatment alone. These patients received none of the customary tranquilizers or "anti-psycho-tic" drugs.[5]

The North Nassau Mental Health Center in Manhasset, Long Island, is a model center for this type of therapy, also known as orthomolecular psychiatry. Some patients enter the Center after other treatment methods (drugs, shock treatment, psychotherapy) have failed for years. Their nutritional needs are analyzed, and a regimen prescribed. Most of them leave several weeks later, feeling and acting normally. The Center has successfully treated more than 10,000 patients. One of them, a 30-year-old man who had been schizophrenic for more than half his life, summed up the experiences of many:

"Megavitamin therapy is a miracle. I'm well. I've been on it more than a year. No more psychotherapy, hospitals, shock treatments, tranquilizers, drugs. I feel it has corrected an imbalance in me. I'm fine now and I'm grateful."[6]

In Cuyahoga County, Ohio, most prisoners have been found to be severe hypoglycemics (see pp. 79-81). In an ongoing program, parolees are placed on a megavitamin, high quality, healthy diet. At this writing, 89 percent have stayed crime-free as long as they have stayed on the diet.[29]

Anyone wishing to consult an orthomolecular psychiatrist in his/her local area should contact the Huxley Institute for Biosocial Research, 1114 First Avenue, New York City, N.Y. 10021.

the cholesterol myth

The uproar against cholesterol is a good example of a mass nutrition myth. A substance of vital importance to our bodies, cholesterol is found in particularly high concentrations in the brain and nervous system. The liver of a normal adult manufactures 800 to 1,000 grams of cholesterol each day—70 to 80% of the cholesterol circulating in most individuals' bodies. When we don't eat any cholesterol, our livers manufacture *more*.[7]

Numerous studies done in the past 30 years show that cholesterol-related problems like atherosclerosis (hardening of the arteries) are caused not by how much cholesterol we take in, but by improper *processing* of cholesterol in the body. Exercise, other lifestyle habits, and a host of nutrients are the keys to keeping the arteries free of cholesterol deposits and maintaining a healthy heart.

The famed Boston Irish Heart Study, for example, examined 500 pairs of Irish brothers, one of whom had emigrated to Boston while the other remained in Ireland. The Ireland-based brothers ate an average of 26% more calories per day, including higher levels of cholesterol and saturated fats than their Boston brothers; yet they had *lower* serum (bloodstream) cholesterol levels and healthier hearts and arteries.[8] What was the Irishmen's secret?

The authors of this study speculated that exercise was a key factor, since most of the Ireland-based brothers did hard physical labor from dawn to dusk, while their Boston brothers held desk jobs. Subsequent studies have confirmed this. The Ireland-based brothers' diets were also notably richer in whole grains.

Cholesterol circulates in the blood in two kinds of packages—low-density lipoproteins (LDLs) and high-density lipoproteins (HDLs). LDLs deliver cholesterol to the tissues; *Time* magazine (3/26/84) calls them "the body's oil trucks." Excesses of LDL cholesterol can end up plastered to artery walls. Meanwhile, HDLs carry excess cholesterol *away* from the tissues to the liver, which will recycle or excrete it. HDLs help to sweep the bloodstream clean of excess cholesterol. Since higher levels of HDL cholesterol protect against heart disease, the goal is to raise the ratio of HDL to LDL cholesterol in the bloodstream.

The single most important factor in doing this seems to be regular exercise, especially aerobic exercise—at least four 20-minute periods per week. Reducing stress is also significant. And although one need *not* ban meat and eggs totally from one's diet, well-balanced eating including lots of whole grains and vegetables and minimizing sweets, white-flour products, and refined foods is very important. In particular, the following nutrients help to raise HDLs and lower LDLs:[9]

Fiber—specifically the *gummy* fibers, such as whole oatmeal and oat bran, pectins (found in apples, raw carrots, and other fresh fruits and vegetables), and guar gum (found in dried beans).

Plant sterols—Chemical cousins of cholesterol, these fatty alcohols, such as beta-sitosterol, are found in a wide varity of vegetables, grains, and seeds, including soybeans, avocados, barley, cabbage, eggplant, sorghum, sunflower seeds, peanuts, rice, corn, yams, mustard, wheat-germ oil, and vegetable oils.

Essential fatty acids—"omega-6" fatty acids, found in seeds, beans, whole grains, vegetable oils, and organ meats; "omega-3" fatty acids, found in fish and fish oils, soybeans, linseeds, and their oils.

Lecithin—found in whole grains, legumes, and eggs.

Raw garlic or raw-garlic oil.

Yogurt.

Vitamin C, vitamin E, and the **B vitamins** are also significant, and recent research shows that proper levels of calcium and magnesium, potassium, and chromium may be important as well.

the sugar question

Try this quick food analysis for fun and enlightenment:
List everything you've had to eat or drink in the past 24 hours. Also include things that you usually have but didn't during this particular period. List the quantities. Next, estimate how much sugar—total—was in the foods and beverages you consumed during this period.

Use Table 1 to find out how much sugar you consumed in popular foods. Arrive at a total amount of teaspoons of sugar.

Table 1

So you think you don't eat much sugar?

Here are the approximate amounts of refined sugar (added sugar, in addition to the sugar naturally present) hidden in popular foods.

Food Item	Size/Portion	Approximate Sugar Content in Teaspoons of Granulated Sugar
Beverages		
cola drinks	1 (6 oz bottle or glass)	3½
cordials	1 (¾ oz glass)	1½
ginger ale	6 oz	5
highball	1 (6 oz glass)	2½
orangeade	1 (8 oz glass)	5
root beer	1 (10 oz bottle)	4½
Seven-Up ®	1 (6 oz bottle or glass)	3¾
soda pop	1 (8 oz bottle)	5
sweet cider	1 cup	6
whiskey sour	1 (3 oz glass)	1½
Cakes and Cookies		
angel food	1 (4 oz piece)	7
apple sauce cake	1 (4 oz piece)	5½
banana cake	1 (2 oz piece)	2
cheese cake	1 (4 oz piece)	2
choc. cake (plain)	1 (4 oz piece)	6
choc. cake (iced)	1 (4 oz piece)	10
coffee cake	1 (4 oz piece)	4½
cup cake (iced)	1	6
fruit cake	1 (4 oz piece)	5
jelly roll	1 (2 oz piece)	2½
orange cake	1 (4 oz piece)	4
pound cake	1 (4 oz piece)	5
sponge cake	1 (1 oz piece)	2
brownies (unfrosted)	1 (¾ oz)	3
chocolate cookies	1	1½
Fig Newtons®	1	5
gingersnaps	1	3
macaroons	1	6
nut cookies	1	1½
oatmeal cookies	1	2
sugar cookies	1	1½
chocolate eclair	1	7
cream puff	1	2
donut (plain)	1	3
donut (glazed)	1	6
Candies		
average milk choc. bar	1 (1½ oz)	2½
chewing gum	1 stick	½
chocolate cream	1 piece	2
butterscotch chew	1 piece	1
chocolate mints	1 piece	2
fudge	1 oz square	4½
gumdrop	1	2
hard candy	4 oz	20
Lifesavers®	1	⅓
peanut brittle	1 oz	3½
Canned Fruits and Juices		
canned apricots	4 halves and 1 T syrup	3½
canned fruit juices (sweet)	½ cup	2
canned peaches	2 halves and 1 T syrup	3½
fruit salad	½ cup	3½
fruit syrup	2 T	2½
stewed fruits	½ cup	2

Food Item	Size/Portion	Approximate Sugar Content in Teaspoons of Granulated Sugar
Dairy Products		
ice cream	⅓ pt (3½ oz)	3½
ice cream cone	1	3½
ice cream soda	1	5
ice cream sundae	1	7
malted milk shake	1 (10 oz glass)	5
Jams and Jellies		
apple butter	1 T	1
jelly	1 T	4.6
orange marmalade	1 T	4.6
peach butter	1 T	1
strawberry jam	1 T	4
Desserts, Miscellaneous		
apple cobbler	½ cup	3
blueberry cobbler	½ cup	3
custard	½ cup	2
french pastry	1 (4 oz piece)	5
fruit gelatin	½ cup	4½
apple pie	1 slice (average)	7
apricot pie	1 slice	7
berry pie	1 slice	10
butterscotch pie	1 slice	4
cherry pie	1 slice	10
cream pie	1 slice	4
lemon pie	1 slice	7
mince meat pie	1 slice	4
peach pie	1 slice	7
prune pie	1 slice	6
pumpkin pie	1 slice	5
rhubarb pie	1 slice	4
banana pudding	½ cup	2
bread pudding	½ cup	1½
chocolate pudding	½ cup	4
cornstarch pudding	½ cup	2½
date pudding	½ cup	7
fig pudding	½ cup	7
Grapenut® pudding	½ cup	2
plum pudding	½ cup	4
rice pudding	½ cup	5
tapioca pudding	½ cup	3
berry tart	1 cup	10
blancmange	½ cup	5
brown Betty	½ cup	3
plain pastry	1 (4 oz piece)	3
sherbet	½ cup	9
Syrups, Sugars and Icings		
brown sugar	1 T	*3
chocolate icing	1 oz	5
chocolate sauce	1 T	3½
corn syrup	1 T	*3
granulated sugar	1 T	*3
honey	1 T	*3
Karo® syrup	1 T	*3
maple syrup	1 T	*5
molasses	1 T	*3½
white icing	1 oz	*5

*actual sugar content

Surprised? So you didn't know that a 12 ounce Coke had 7 tea-spoons of sugar in it. Did you ever imagine that the jelly on your morning toast had 4 to 6 teaspoons of sugar, or that the chocolate cake with icing had 10 tea-spoons? Would you drink a cup of plain sugar? Yet, we consume a trem-endous amount of this substance with-out knowing it.

The average American diet now contains about 125 pounds of sugar per year, an average of 35 teaspoonfuls per day. This means that 15%–25% of the total calories consumed per day are from sugar, but sugar provides no nutrition at all.[10] Though it can be burned as energy, we don't need it. We get plenty of fuel from other foods. Most sugar we eat gets stored as fat. Most important, we can only have a certain number of calories per day. When we eat empty sugar—with no vitamins, no minerals, no fiber, no protein and no fat—we're passing up some other, nourishing food that we probably need for our health.

Some authorities feel that sugar is not actually a food, but a chemical, since it has to undergo tremendous processing to arrive in its white, pure, granulated form. Harvard nutritionist Jean Mayer has stated that sugar, which was once an additive, is now being viewed in our society as a "new food"—but that it's a food our bodies cannot tolerate.[11]

Some people have switched to brown sugar, thinking that would re-duce their sugar consumption. Actually, brown sugar is white sugar, col-ored and flavored with 6%–8% molasses. All other sugars like turbinado, raw sugar, and the like are almost identical to refined white sugar! Any color or flavor was added *after* refinement into white sugar . . . because it's against the law to sell unprocessed sugar in the United States.[12]

Sugar seems to trigger or contribute to many illnesses. It has been linked to coronary heart disease, mental illness, dental caries, diabetes, hyperinsulinism, obesity, and others.[13]

So what should you substitute for sugar? Artificial sweeteners are risky, because their long-term chemical effects on the body are un-known. Sweeteners that can be used are honey, blackstrap molasses, sorghum and unsweetened fruit juice. All of these substances contain nutrients within them: in other words, they are still alive. These nutri-ents aid the body in its functioning.

Table 2 shows comparative nutritional values of sugar, honey and molasses, as determined by the U.S. Department of Agriculture.

Table 2
Sugars, Honey, and Molasses Compared

	White Sugar	Brown Sugar	Molasses, Blackstrap	Honey, Strained	Maple Sugar
Minerals	mg.	mg.	mg.	mg.	mg.
Calcium	0	85	684	5	143
Phosphorus	0	19	84	6	11
Iron	0.1	3.4	16.1	0.5	1.4
Potassium	3.0	344	2927	51	242
Sodium	1.0	30	96	5	14
Vitamins					
Thiamin	0	0.01	0.11	trace	—
Riboflavin	0	0.03	0.19	0.04	—
Niacin	0	0.2	2.0	0.3	—

Source: "Composition of Foods," Agriculture Handbook, No. 8, USDA.

hyperinsulinism: everyone's problem?

The foods you eat each day have a significant impact on how you feel that day—relaxed or tense, energetic or weary, calm or anxious, pleasant or irritable. You may be tired, depressed, or even in pain because the foods you eat are playing havoc with your blood sugar level.

The body needs to maintain a particular level of sugar in the blood, just as it needs to maintain a particular oxygen level. Depending on your body chemistry, you need between 50 and 150 mg. of glucose (the body's sugar) per 100 cc. of blood at all times—less than two teaspoonfuls in the entire body![14] The proper blood sugar level is crucial, especially for brain functioning; we literally cannot "think straight" if it's too high or too low.

Sweets and processed carbohydrates can have a devastating effect on blood sugar and consequently on one's physical energy and emotional state. By processed carbohydrates, we mean candy, soda pop, sugared drinks, and refined flour products such as cakes, cookies, breads, cereals, crackers, and pasta. Even whole-grain products, honey or molasses (all healthy in other ways) can upset your blood sugar if eaten in large quantities.

When sweets or processed carbohydrates hit the stomach—anyone's stomach—they are instantly converted to glucose, which hits the blood in minutes. You can feel it—that much-touted "burst of energy" after eating a sweet. You may feel revved up, nervous, excited. But the body needs a stable—not seesaw—level of blood sugar in order to function. Actually, your brain is saying, "Oh, no... what *hit* me?!" Your pancreas is registering, "Emergency!... sugar overload!... Emergency!"

As more and more glucose comes out of your stomach into your blood during the next few minutes, your pancreas pours out insulin to process it, keeping your system out of danger. However, the pancreas has no way of knowing when the sugar flood will end. It can overreact, producing too much insulin, which in turn processes too much sugar. In some people this reaction is mild, in some it's drastic. Either way, the outcome is *low blood sugar.* Low? That's right. You are left, an hour after eating a sweet, with low blood sugar and a ravenous appetite. If you're like most people, you try to satisfy that appetite with another sweet—and the cycle starts again.

The well-documented results of low blood sugar include fatigue, nervousness, anxiety, depression, lack of motivation, irrationality, colds, muscle pains, asthma, hay fever... all the way up to heart palpitations, coma and mental illness complete with hallucinations. It all depends on how severe and chronic the condition is.[15]

Most of these are the familiar complaints for which we can never seem to find a cause or cure. Some doctors estimate that hyperinsulinism (now better known as hypoglycemia) affects 50% to 80% of Americans mildly to moderately and is often not diagnosed.[16] As for more severe cases, E.M. Abrahamson, M.D., and A.W. Pezet, two authoritative writers on the subject, said:

"Persons who at last were found to be suffering from hyperinsulinism have been treated for coronary thrombosis and other heart ailments, brain tumor, epilepsy, gall bladder disease, appendicitis, hysteria and every sort of neurosis. They have been told repeatedly that their trouble is 'all in the mind' and sent to the psychoanalyst."[17]

How does one acquire low blood sugar? According to these authors, one can create this illness simply by eating the modern North American diet, with its sweets and carbohydrates. Ingesting lots of sweets teaches our pancreas to repond to any upswing in blood sugar as a drastic emergency. The only way to desensitize and normalize our insulin production and our blood sugar is to change our eating habits. For children, it makes sense not to let them become sugar addicts in the first place. (Expectant mothers delivering their babies in hospitals should instruct the hospitals not to give sugar-water to their newborn children.)

In case you don't think any of this applies to you... do you drink coffee? Caffeine has the same effect as sugar. It stimulates the adrenal glands to produce adrenaline, the "fight-or-flight" hormone, and adrenaline in turn triggers the liver to pour stored sugar (glycogen) into the bloodstream. The pancreas reacts, and the seesaw starts again. That's why so many people go through their workdays fighting off fatigue, feeling half-asleep. They munch sweets and gulp coffee by the hour in the mistaken notion that this increases their energy Actually, these substances sap energy by decreasing the blood sugar. By the end of the day, these workers are worn out. They think: "Why am I always so tired? I must hate my job."

If you've experienced any of the complaints that could be related to hyperinsulinism, or if you're simply interested in trying out a high-energy, fatigue-reducing diet, follow these guidelines, for at least a month. It can't hurt, and might do wonders for you!

1.) *No sugared drinks, candy, commercial cereals, ice cream, cake, cookies, pasta, potato chips or crackers.* (If you think you can't live without sweets and breadstuffs, remember that the craving for these substances may well be caused by the low blood sugar that results from eating them in the first place. For many people, the craving disappears when they're on this diet.)

2.) *Eat little or no bread, potatoes, fruit juices, and processed grains.* If you must have some, eat in small quantities at a meal with other foods—proteins and vegetables. You can have moderate amounts of whole grains, beans, and whole fruits. Use only whole-grain breads. If you must have cereal, try whole rolled oats or unprocessed bran sweetened with raisins or fresh fruit.

3.) *When you want something sweet, eat a piece of fresh fruit.* Fruit is high in carbohydrate, but its absorption into the system is slowed by its fiber content, and its concentration is diluted by its high water content.

4.) *Eat relatively small meals, even if that means increasing your (healthy) snacks.* Snack on fruits, nuts, sunflower seeds, vegetables, unsweetened nut butters, cheeses, etc.

5.) *Avoid caffeine—coffee, cola drinks and teas, as much as possible.* (De-caffeinated coffee and herb teas are OK.)

6.) *Avoid alcohol as much as possible, too, since alcohol is digested as a pure sugar.*[18]

After 2 to 4 weeks of this diet, mildly hypoglycemic persons can add back modest amounts of juices and natural sweeteners, and can increase their intake of whole-grain carbohydrates. By then, you should be developing an awareness of your body and moods that will help you regulate yourself.

Natural sweeteners are honey, molasses, maple syrup, sorghum, dates, figs, dried (but not glazed!) fruits, and unsweetened fruit and vegetable juices. Whole-grain carbohydrates include anything made with strictly whole-grain flour—cookies, cakes, bread and pasta.

Remember that it's best not to eat a lot of these kinds of foods at one time, and remember to eat them with other types of foods. Proteins, fats and the fiber in whole grains and vegetables help to slow down the stomach's digestion of carbohydrates. The same advice applies to caffeine and alcohol—use in moderation and accompanied by other foods.

white flour vs. whole wheat flour

Many years ago it was discovered by millers that by taking the wheat germ out of the wheat, they would get a product that would not turn rancid. It was of little concern to them that they were also removing all the nutritional value and fiber content of the flour. This "de-natured" white flour will not support even bacteria life—that's why it won't spoil![19]

During the two World Wars, several countries, including Denmark and Norway, stopped milling flour, so that only whole wheat flour was available. These nations also reduced or banned meat consumption. Research has shown a tremendous correlation between the drop in heart disease during this period, until white flour and meats were reinstituted.[20]

In the milling process, vitamins and minerals are removed from the flour. To make so-called "enriched" flour, the miller adds 4 or 5 artifical vitamins and minerals to white flour.[21] Mathematically, we have suffered a major loss of nutrients. (See Table 3.) In addition, all of the fiber has

Table 3

Whole Wheat Flour Compared to White Flour

100g. or 3½ oz	Whole Wheat Flour		White Flour			Enriched White Flour		
Protein	13.3	grams	10.5	g.	79%*	10.5	g.	79%*
Minerals								
Calcium	41	milligrams	16	mg.	39%	16	mg.	39%
Phosphorous	372	mg.	87	mg.	23%	87	mg.	39%
Iron	3.3	mg.	0.8	mg.	24%	2.9	mg.	88%
Potassium	370	mg.	95	mg.	26%	95	mg.	26%
Sodium	3	mg.	2	mg.	67%	2	mg.	67%
Vitamins								
Thiamin	0.55	mg.	0.06	mg.	11%	0.44	mg.	80%
Riboflavin	0.12	mg.	0.05	mg.	42%	0.26	mg.	216%
Niacin	4.3	mg.	0.9	mg.	21%	3.5	mg.	81%

Source: "Composition of Foods," Agriculture Handbook, No. 8, USDA.
*—Percent of the amount supplied by whole wheat flour.

been removed and the protein value of the flour has been reduced.

bran fiber

Fiber gives the digestive system necessary exercise and keeps the foods you've consumed moving along, thus alleviating constipation. Some researchers have found that cancer of the colon may result from sluggish bowel action, which allows cancer-causing wastes to remain in contact with the colon walls too long. Adequate fiber in the diet has also been connected with reduced incidences of gall bladder disease, hemorrhoids, and varicose veins.[22]

The original study on fiber was done by Dr. Neil S. Painter, a London surgeon. He studied the effects of bran fiber on patients with diverticular disease. In this painful, common ailment, pockets or sacs are formed in the colon as a result of too much pressure (constipation, hard stools, etc.). When these patients used bran, they had soft stools, and easy defecation without straining. Constipation disappeared. The use of laxatives decreased dramatically. While bran sometimes caused stomach gas, it generally disappeared within 3 weeks.[23]

While you can get some fiber from fruits, vegetables, and whole grains, unprocessed bran is the all time winner. Twenty grams of bran has the same bulking effect as 200–300 grams of most other foodstuffs.[24] In addition, there is a trend today towards a reduction in the consumption of fresh fruits and vegetables. Items like frozen orange juice, without the pulp, and iceberg lettuce contain very little fiber. Processed bran that is in some commercial cereals is also not very effective due to the refinement it has undergone.

How much bran do you need? Just adding 2 to 3 tablespoons of raw bran to your diet each day is all that is necessary. Start with 1 tablespoon per day (some at each meal or all at once), and gradually increase the amount to 2–3 tablespoons per day. You can add the bran to cereal, yogurt, soup, casseroles, ground meat, bread, muffins, pancakes, etc. Always have some liquid with the bran.

Bran is also great for dieting. Take raw bran with a glass of water shortly before each meal. The bran expands to partially fill the stomach, so that you don't want as much food. In addition, British physicians such as Dr. K. W. Heaton of the University Department of Medicine in Bristol have found that fiber can slow down calorie absorption, allowing the body to excrete an extra 200 or more calories each day.[25]

additives: what you don't know could hurt you

Why is diet cola bad for you? Why should you avoid something labeled "artificial" or "imitation"?

Chemical additives are not natural substances; they are synthetic. There are two problems with additives: most of them are untested, and many may be carcinogenic. In 1971 there were 3,000 additives which could be put in our foods. By 1975 this had increased to nearly 10,000![26] Many of these substances have not been tested for their safety. Of course, no recently-developed chemical has been tested for long–term effects . . . what it does to a person over 10, 20 or 50 years of consumption. In addition, when each substance is tested, it is tested in isolation. This testing ignores the synergistic process—the fact that chemicals in combination can have a totally different effect than one chemical alone. How do these additives react with each other in our bodies? How do they react with other chemicals we take in through our lungs, in our water, in medications? We have no idea.

The point of this discussion is not to criticize all technology and invention. But we have seen in the past few years that seemingly helpful or at least innocuous substances (certain chemicals, plastics, detergents, insecticides, industrial wastes) can wreak havoc on our water supply, our air, our food supply, animal life, and our bodies. The damages, when they have appeared, have been devastating—a dead lake, a water supply completely polluted, the high mercury content of many fish, the high chemical content in the milk of nursing mothers. It is time to begin using technology with foresight, especially as it relates to our own health. Until this foresight becomes standard commercial procedure, we can protect ourselves by purchasing and demanding foods without chemical additives.

The additive problem was aptly illustrated by the case of Red Dye #2. There was a 20-year controversy about whether or not this chemical could cause cancer. During this time, it was continuously added to foods and alcoholic beverages. Finally, the U.S. Food and Drug Administration (certainly not an alarmist organization) had it removed from the market as a potential cancer-causing agent. However, since the dye has been in hot dogs, hamburgers and liquor for years, the potential damage could reach millions of people.

Red Dye #2 is just one of many additives tested and deemed unsafe *after they had been added to foods for some time.*[27]

One or two of these substances probably would not be a problem; the problem is the enormous number of these unknowns, and their increasing usage by the food industry to bolster color, flavor and freshness after natural color and flavor have been reduced by commercial growing and processing methods.

why eat organic?

Non-organic, commercially grown crops are developed and bred for a variety of factors—color, size, and rapid growth (so that another crop may be grown in the same season). These crops are not developed with nutrition in mind, and the other factors involved may conflict with nutrition.

First, the land they are grown on is used constantly and to maximum capacity; it has long ago been totally depleted of natural minerals. There is no iron, calcium, zinc, magnesium . . . or any of a dozen other trace elements necessary for the human body. So, these elements cannot come into our bodies through commercial crops. Standard fertilizers add to the soil only nitrogen, potassium and phosphorus.

Second, non-organic crops have been sprayed with powerful pesticides, insecticides and the like. As with food additives, we don't know which ones will eventually prove unsafe: remember DDT? Non-organic farmers also use powerful weed-killers, which are generally designed to kill any plant life other than a specific group of vegetables. What might they do to our bodies?

Organic farmers try to re-balance the soil with the proper minerals. Only natural methods of pest control are employed, such as plant extracts, and growing certain crops and flowers side by side to protect each other. Some of these methods have been known for thousands of years. In addition, maintaining the soil in a healthy state seems to give plants natural protection against insect pests.

Obtaining organic produce may be difficult, since most farmers are not using these methods. One means of solving this problem is to garden and preserve your own produce. Vitamin and mineral supplements are also important.

Don't be shy about asking for organic products in the stores. As demand increases, more of the major manufacturers will abide by the economics of the situation, and produce more natural and organic products.

vitamins

Though mainstream medicine is beginning to recognize that vitamins and minerals play a crucial role in health, many doctors are still quite skeptical and/or uninformed when it comes to considering supplements for individual patients.

Let me relate my own experience: I have always had extremely cold hands and feet. When I became a vegetarian (no, you don't have to become a vegetarian) the problem became even worse. During the winter, I'd be indoors writing, and my hand would cramp up from being so cold. This situation finally forced me to experiment with vitamins. The result of this is that my extremities are warm about 80% of the time, even during the middle of the winter.

While seeing a doctor for a regular check-up, I asked the doctor if there were any vitamins that I could take to be 100% warm. In response, I got a 15 to 20 minute lecture on the total uselessness of vitamins to correct circulation problems. The doctor's advice—learn to live with the problem. (I did not mention that vitamins had already corrected most of it.)

Another true story illustrates how effective vitamins can be. Recently, I drove to a conference with Debbie, a 21-year-old travel agent. During the drive, Debbie told me that she had been experiencing severe depressions at least once a day. The depressions appeared to be unrelated to things happening in her life. She could have a day full of good experiences and still become depressed. As could be expected, this was causing her a great deal of concern.

I questioned her about her diet. It turned out to be a "typical" North American diet of processed foods, sweet snacks, white sugar and flour, chemicals and preservatives. I told her that the problem might be a vitamin deficiency. Since she was open to trying some remedy, I gave her a supply of my vitamins to last the 3 days of the conference. (See next page for recommended amounts.)

On the third day of the conference, she told me that she felt great, and that she felt like a new person. She had not been depressed even once during the entire conference, despite the fact that there were many problems. Debbie told me that she had even *tried* to get depressed just to see if she could do it—and she could not. When she returned home, friends immediately remarked that she was totally different. Her co-workers even called to thank me for the change in Debbie. I told them the vitamins were responsible, not me. Debbie's boss was so impressed that she now keeps vitamins next to the water cooler.

The normal ways in which foods are grown, processed, preserved, stored, shipped and cooked result in vast losses of vitamins and minerals. As much as 40-50% of the B and C vitamins in foods is lost this way. Even organic foods are often grown on soils depleted of their nutritional elements by years of previous abuse.

Thus it is difficult to get the necessary amounts of vitamins and minerals for optimum health from the things we eat. While there is still controversy about whether supplements are absorbed by the body in the same way as nutrients from food, a wide range of evidence suggests that supplements can play a role in altering health and well-being.

The following suggestions for vitamins and minerals to consume daily come from Dr. Michael Colgan, an Australian-born physician who now heads his own institute, the Colgan Institute of Nutritional Science in San Diego, California. He has done much groundbreaking research on how different vitamins and minerals work together in the body, how supplements can be used to treat various ailments, and how to determine your individual supplement needs based on diet, lifestyle, and health factors.

The amounts listed here represent Dr. Colgan's "basic formula"; the lower amounts are for someone weighing 120 pounds or less, up to the higher numbers for someone weighing 180 pounds. If you weigh more than 180 pounds, double the lower figures. To further refine these amounts to your needs, see Dr. Colgan's book *Your Personal Vitamin Profile* (New York: Quill, 1982). Where his amounts differ greatly from other research I consider to be credible, I have listed the alternative amounts in brackets.

Daily Suggested Supplements

B-complex tablets, or combination of tablets, that add up to:

> 10-15 milligrams (mg.) each of B_1 and B_2
> 50-75 mg. B_3 (niacin or niacinamide)
> 20-30 mg. each B_5 (panthothenic acid) and B_6
> 20-30 micrograms (mcg.) B_{12}
> 100-150 mg. each choline and inositol [Alternative: up
>   to 1000 mg. each]
> 200-300 mcg. folic acid
> 500-750 mcg. biotin [Alt.: 25 mcg.].
> 50-75 mg. PABA.

Vitamin C: 1,000-1,500 mg., with 100-150 mg. bioflavonoids.
Vitamin A: 2,000-3,000 units, with 200-300 units vitamin D
  [Alt.: 25,000 units A with 400-800 units D].
Vitamin E: 200-300 units [Alt.: up to 600 units].

Minerals:

      500–750 mg. calcium with 1/2 as much magnesium as calcium, and
        2/5 (40%) as much phosphorus as calcium
      10–15 mg. iron
      1–1.5 mg. copper
      5–7.5 mg. each zinc and manganese [Alt.: 15–30 mg. zinc)
      25–37 mcg. each selenium and chromium
      50–75 mcg. each iodine and molybdenum [Alt.: 15 mcg. iodine].

Divide your daily total into two or three portions a day. **Always take supplements just after a good-sized meal, with a large glass of cold liquid.** (Vitamins and minerals work with food in the body. Hot beverages can destroy some of their potency.)

While this might seem like a large quantity to take each day, many of these amounts are available in standard combinations. Check health-food stores, food cooperatives, and mail-order advertisements in magazines like *Prevention* (see Bibliography) for the combinations, prices and quality you prefer.

Keep in mind that each person is biochemically unique; it may be necessary to adjust recommended amounts to suit you. Tune in to your body to see what feels best. (See "Body Talk" section, p. 96.)

A nutritionist or nutritionally oriented physician can help determine your exact vitamin and mineral requirements. S/he may prescribe a hair, blood, or tissue analysis, a glucose tolerance test, and other measures to plan the best diet for you. For referrals to holistic or nutritionally aware doctors in your area, contact:

American Holistic Medical Association
6932 Little River Turnpike
Annandale, VA 22003
(703) 642-5880

International Academy of Preventive Medicine
Box 25276
Shawnee Mission, KS 66225
(913) 648-8720

a woRd about shopping

Always read the labels and be aware of the ingredients in the products you buy—no matter where you buy them, no matter what the larger words on the package say. Not everything marked "All Natural" is such. I've picked up loaves of "natural" bread that contained sugar; and of "whole wheat" bread that listed enriched (white) flour as a major ingredient.

Not everything in a health food store is sugarless, whole grain, organic, or healthy for every purpose. If you are trying to avoid sweet snacks in order to even out your blood sugar, an all-natural honey-granola bar is not a good thing to eat.

Quaker 100% Natural Cereal

INGREDIENTS: Rolled oats, brown sugar, rolled whole wheat, vegetable oil, dried unsweetened coconut, non-fat dry milk, almonds, honey.

100% Natural Cereal

INGREDIENTS

Rolled oats, brown sugar, rolled whole wheat, vegetable oil, dried unsweetened coconut, almonds, non-fat dry milk, honey, hazelnuts.

Nutrition Information Per serving:

The question here: is sugar a "natural" substance?

Cronchola

A delicious, wholesome snack of **PEANUT BUTTER, GRANOLA, & CHOCOLATE CHIPS**

Ingredients:
Rolled oats, hydrogenated vegetable oil, sugar, peanut butter, corn sweeteners, brown sugar, non-fat dry milk, defatted wheat germ, soy flour, chocolate, sodium caseinate, wheat flour, vegetable oil, salt, U.S. certified color, pure vanilla, lecithin, BHA, propyl gallate, citric acid.

SUNFIELD FOODS
A SUNMARK, INC.
COMPANY
ST. LOUIS,
MISSOURI 63127
Patent Pending
©1976

ALL-BRAN
—A NATURAL—
FOOD FIBER CEREAL
WITH SUGAR, MALT FLAVORING AND SALT ADDED

Sugar plus more sugar plus corn syrup/sweeteners (equivalent to sugar) plus vegetable oils plus chemicals . . . How much more "wholesome" or "balanced" can you get?

FOOD STICKS
Pillsbury

A BALANCED NUTRITION BETWEEN MEAL FOOD.

INGREDIENTS: SUGAR, CORN SYRUP, HYDROGENATED VEGETABLE OIL WITH BHA (PRESERVES FRESHNESS), COCOA AND CHOCOLATE (PROCESSED WITH ALKALI), ISOLATED SOY PROTEIN, SODIUM CASEINATE, WATER, GLYCERIN, MODIFIED CORN STARCH, VEGETABLE MONOGLYCERIDES, CALCIUM PHOSPHATE, SALT, MAGNESIUM OXIDE, CITRIC ACID, VITAMIN C, IRON ORTHOPHOSPHATE, VITAMIN E ACETATE, VITAMIN A PALMITATE, NIACINAMIDE, VITAMIN D₃, VITAMIN B₆ HYDROCHLORIDE, RIBOFLAVIN, THIAMIN MONONITRATE, FOLACIN, POTASSIUM IODIDE, VITAMIN B₁₂, ARTIFICIAL FLAVOR.

FOR NUTRITION INFORMATION SEE BACK PANEL ▼

MADE WITH ENRICHED FLOUR, WATER, CORN SWEETENER, WHEAT BRAN, WHOLE WHEAT FLOUR, WHEAT GLUTEN, SUGAR, YEAST, SHORTENING, SALT, WHEY, SOY FLOUR, BUTTER, HONEY, DOUGH CONDITIONERS, CALCIUM CASEINATE AND YEAST NUTRIENTS.

Note that "wheat flour" and "enriched" or "unbleached" flour are the same *plain white* flour discussed in this chapter. Only *whole wheat* flour is really whole wheat. Also note sugar, corn syrup.

INGREDIENTS: ENRICHED WHEAT FLOUR, WATER, CORN SYRUP, CRACKED WHEAT, YEAST, SOY FLOUR, SALT, HONEY, WHEAT BRAN, NON-FAT DRY MILK, SHORTENING, MOLASSES, MALT, DAIRY WHEY, DOUGH CONDITIONERS, YEAST NUTRIENTS, VINEGAR, ENRICHED WITH CALCIUM SULFATE.

resource materials

Diet for a Small Planet is an excellent book for starting on a vegetarian or limited-meat diet. It explains why there's no worry about inadequate protein for vegetarians and tells how to combine different foods with each other to get the highest possible protein values if your protein needs are extra-high. For example, if you have 2 cups rice one day and ¾ cup peas or beans the next day, you are having the equivalent of a 6½ ounce steak; if you eat both the same day, your body gets the protein equivalent of a 9½ ounce steak. This book is chock-full of recipes and well-documented information about nutrition, economics and the relationships of various dietary styles to world hunger.

Prevention magazine, published by Rodale Press, 33 East Minor Street, Emmaus, PA 18049, has been published monthly for 31 years. Back copies, available in some libraries, are likely to be useful. For current issues, write to the above address. This magazine is a wide-ranging digest of nutrition and health information, with much practical advice on choosing, raising and cooking foods. The magazine keeps up with the latest developments in medicine and the law as they relate to nutrition. Many articles offer old and new remedies for pain and illness, using nutritional elements and herbs. Many vitamin companies advertise in *Prevention*, offering mail-order prices considerably lower than store prices.

More good resources are listed in the Bibliography of this book.

herbs to soothe and relax

Herbs have been used for centuries as natural relaxants and medicines. The herbs which act specifically on the nervous system to relax and calm the body are called "nervines." The herbs mentioned herein can be bought at certain pharmacies and most health food stores, without a prescription. Since these herbs are usually taken internally as teas, it is important to recognize the potency and purpose of each tea and use them with care.

Nature has provided these substances to help heal many different ailments. Some herbs can be used anytime and in a general way to help one to relax. But some work in a more specific way to effect a cure, such as by speeding up the action of the digestive tract, thus restoring the body to a more balanced state.

Our all time favorite is camomile tea. Camomile is a great relaxer and, if used before bedtime or before a massage, helps one to sink easily into the deeper levels of relaxation.

As with all herbal teas, we steep the flowers in boiled (not boiling) water for 3 to 5 minutes and then serve either plain or with honey. It's important to use only a teaspoon of tea per cup, at most. Don't steep too long or the tea will be too strong and taste bitter. We strain all the teas except camomile; it's fun to have a few of the flowers bobbing in the teacup.

Camomile can also be used externally in a massage oil as follows: heat up some almond oil mixed with some favorite massage oil and a few camomile flowers. Pour this into a bowl and begin your massage. Camomile, besides being an excellent relaxer and an aromatic (the fragrance of sweet flowers), helps to tone the stomach and relieve indigestion.

Mint teas give a very peaceful and quieting "high" feeling. They are also very aromatic, and we haven't found anyone yet who didn't enjoy them. They relieve "gas" pains in the stomach, soothe the nerves, and can calm someone in an agitated state. Our favorite mint tea is spearmint. It can be used alone ... or combined with camomile. Licorice root, a very sweet herb that can be used in combination with many others, goes particularly well with mint. Use sparingly.

Another very useful tea is sage. It relieves pain, increases circulation, and quiets the nerves. Do not steep this tea too long.

Blue cohosh helps to relieve menstrual cramps.

Still another tea to use by itself is lobelia. Lobelia should be used conservatively. It can be stimulant and a muscle relaxant, but also an intense depressant if used too often or in too high a dosage. Drink only one cup a day.

In cases of anxiety or insomnia, hops is probably the most potent cure. Hops is a main ingredient in beer and has been known for centuries to have great natural tranquilizing properties. Pillows have been stuffed with it to help induce sleep. We like to use hops combined with scullcap and catnip (other potent nervines) to produce a calm, "floating" level of consciousness. This combination can put the most worried person to sleep.

Other herbs we use are blue violet and red clover. We have what we call the "rainbow cure" for cases of general nervousness. We combine red clover, blue violet and golden seal in the ratio 3–3–1. These 3 herbs combine wonderfully, but please use honey. Golden seal (a powerful antibiotic that proves useful in many illnesses) tastes very bitter and medicine-y otherwise. This tea will also purify the blood and strengthen the internal organs.

As you can see, certain herbs can be combined. We call these "synergistic" herbs. These herbs blend into each other and create new flavors, powers and cures that could not be obtained from any one by itself. Here are some of our favorite synergistic herb combinations:

Lemon grass and mint cool the body in summer and ease tension as they refresh. Sassafras, wintergreen and mugwort make a great muscle relaxant. In hysterical states use valerian, hops and scullcap. In cases of high blood pressure, we use snake root, black cohosh and pennyroyal. For headache, use rosemary and yarrow.

Many people suffer anxiety and tension because of a lack of calcium in their diets. This also happens when the other elements that would aid in assimilating calcium in the body are lacking. Herbs such as camomile, comfrey, and oakraw contain calcium; and comfrey is said to aid in the use of it in the body.

One herb that we do not use as a tea is mugwort. We stuff mugwort into pillows and sleep on them to have vivid, colorful, memorable

94

dreams. For a truly euphoric evening, try sleeping on a mugwort and hops pillow, after a shiatsu massage with camomile oil rubbed on your body, after drinking a cup of hot sage tea, after a warm bath!

yogi tea

Yogi tea is the name for an unusually relaxing and delightful tea. As you'll see from the recipe, most of the ingredients can be found on your own spice rack. If you drink several cups of the tea, you will discover why I call it an unusual tea. Try it, you will like it!

While the following recipe is for one cup of the tea, I would suggest preparing a large batch. Whatever you do not use can be refrigerated until the milk is added.

To make one cup of Yogi tea, place the following ingredients in a pot with a tight fitting lid:

8 whole cloves
8 cardamon seeds (crushed)
6 black pepper corns (whole)
1 piece gingerroot (approximately ¼" to ½")
1 piece cinnamon stick (approximately 1" long)
2 cups of water

Boil all ingredients 20 to 30 minutes with the lid on.

Add a pinch of black tea. Boil 5 more minutes.

Add 2 oz, of milk (add this only to amount you are going to be using that day). Bring to a boil and immediately remove from heat.

Add honey to taste.

Enjoy!

If you did store some tea, just boil for several minutes, then add milk and serve.

The leftover ingredients from the first brew can be used a second time.

"body talk": behavioral kinesiology

This section presents a unique system for assessing the impact of your inner attitudes and of all kinds of environmental stimuli (including food, people around you, even the paintings on a wall) on your health and well-being. Called behavioral kinesiology, it was developed by John Diamond, M.D., and is outlined in his books, *BK: Behavioral Kinesiology* (Harper & Row, 1979), and *Your Body Doesn't Lie* (Warner Books, 1980).

To understand the material in the chapter, you must try it on a partner. Seeing for yourself is the only way you will believe what is described here.

Kinesiology is the science of muscle testing. It allows us to easily *see*, immediately and directly, how everything around us and within us affects our strength, health and ability to act. This chapter also includes techniques for regulating stress affects and strengthening your system.

After you have tried a few tests, turn to the section on "How Kinesiology Works."

finding normal resistance

1. You must have a partner to do this. Face your partner.

2. Your partner should raise one arm straight out, perpendicular to the body, thumb pointing towards floor. The other arm should hang at the side.

3. Place one of your hands on your partner's extended arm, just above the wrist. Place your other hand on partner's opposite shoulder (See Step 3.)

Step 3

4. Instruct your partner to *resist* as you push down, firmly, on the extended arm. You are *not* trying to *force* the arm all the way down; you simply need to feel the normal level of resistance. You should start firmly, not suddenly or with a jerk; and push for several seconds; then release.

the power of the mind

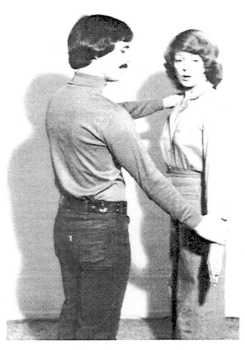

Lowered Resistance

1. While your partner keeps her arm extended, have her think of an unhappy experience or someone she dislikes. Allow a few seconds for her to fix the thought firmly in her mind. Tell her to keep thinking about it, and to resist as you press on her arm. The arm will usually go down easily, even though your partner resists with all her might.

2. Wait several seconds; then tell your partner to resume the arm-up position while thinking of some enjoyable experience or someone she likes. Again, allow a few seconds for her to focus on the image, then tell her to resist as you push down on her arm. The arm will usually stay level and strong, even if you push *harder* than you did just a moment before.

3. Switch roles. Have your partner test you.

These are not tricks; the results are real and repeatable. In fact, many thousands of people have been tested this way, including hundreds of business people who test each other during my lectures.

The results have nothing to do with muscular strength, since you are testing only the level of resistance the person has already

Testing Strong

demonstrated. The thumb is turned down to make sure you are testing only one muscle, the deltoid. The deltoid muscle will either be capable of locking the arm into place—which means the body's life energy level is strong—or the arm will go down easily, which means the body's energy level has been weakened. The contrast is very easy to see.[31]

All of the tests described in this chapter have been conducted with scales and instruments that show exactly how many pounds of pressure are being applied to the arm, and exactly how much resistance the person is able to muster, but the results from touch alone are identical to the laboratory results. When a person's arm goes down easily, it is not because you are suddenly pressing harder; it is because his life energy is weak at that moment.

In doing a series of tests, if you are afraid that a person's arm will grow tired and affect the results, feel free to switch arms. Just be sure to test the "new" arm for normal resistance so you'll have a basis for comparison before going on to particular tests.

If you can't quite believe what's happening, test each other on a whole series of happy and sad thoughts and experiences. Test on a series of people you like and dislike. If you test weak on a person you like, think about your relationship. Could the person be weakening your energy level in some way? Do you actually have mixed, or ambivalent feelings towards the person? Is there an element of fear, envy, competition, or undermining going on?

Do you find it surprisingly easy to keep your arm steady while thinking of a pleasant scene or happy experience? Do you find that your arm is "like jelly," almost as if it can't *hear* your brain's command to "resist" while you think of a painful or aggravating situation?

If you or a partner tests strong on *everything*, please turn to the section of this chapter on "Strengthening the Thymus" (p. 113), and the last section (p. 115), for an explanation.

You have just experienced the *power* our thoughts have on our energy systems. There are many applications.

In recent years, many books and articles have praised the idea of "positive thinking." They discuss the power of the mind over everyday life, and the need to feed our minds positive thoughts as we feed our bodies healthful foods. They report extraordinary stories of success, achievement, happiness and even "luck" resulting from positive thinking. Yet, for most people, this is just a concept, not something they have knowingly experienced. With kinesiology testing, however, anyone can see the obvious, immediate impact of positive and negative thoughts and experiences on the body.

If you know someone who seems caught up in negative thoughts most of the time, look at his health. Does he become ill frequently? Does he have alcers, arthritis, high blood pressure? This person has fallen into a vicious cycle, in which depressed or despairing thoughts weaken his body, which in turn becomes less able to cope with stress and negative thoughts!

When your mind is not concentrating on some specific task, does it tend to "wander" to whatever is most troubling or unsettled in your life? This is a habit most people have. I'm not referring to the act of consciously trying to *think through* a problem. I'm talking about a *habit* our minds have of settling on our own inadequacies, our dissatisfactions, our minor annoyances—and replaying them like a broken record. This is non-productive and weakening; and it wears away our problem-solving capacity! Next time you notice this habit, turn your mind deliberately to something happy—a memory, a plan, a dream, a hope, a good relationship, a work of art. Develop a new strengthening habit of letting your mind "wander" through positive territory.

smiles & frowns

As simple a stimulus as a smile or frown from another person can measurably affect your energy level. See for yourself:

1. Find your partner's Normal Resistance, as described on page 96.

2. Have your partner look at the photograph, on this page, of a woman frowning. (Cover up the *other* photo, of the woman smiling, while you do this.) Place your hand on her extended arm, just above the wrist, and push down firmly while she looks at the photo. (Her arm should drop easily.)

3. Now have your partner look at the photograph of the woman smiling. (Cover the frowning photo.) Have her extend her arm again; push down firmly on it as before. (The arm should stay extended.)

You can get the same results without photographs, simply by smiling or frowning at your partner as you test him. *In fact, when doing any kinesiology testing, it is important to keep a "straight" or neutral expression on you face to avoid prejudicing the results.* For many tests, the person being tested can also keep his eyes closed as "insurance" that what is in his hand or his thoughts is all that's being tested.

Next time you walk into a room and feel suddenly, unexpectedly uncomfortable, check people's expressions. You may be in a room full of frowning people!

Conversely, being around people who are smiling—or smiling yourself—is highly strengthening. You may have noticed that having a person in an office who smiles and is cheerful most of the time gives you a "lift," a sense of well-being. Even if you have no particular relationship with the person, and even if you have no "good reason" to feel good, you feel "lifted up" at least momentarily, every time that person smiles at you. Now you understand the reason: this person has literally, physically raised your energy level. A consistently cheerful person can thus tangibly help other people to get more done and to pursue their work more enthusiastically.

foods

Foods also have a kinesiological effect on the body. Try this:

1. Start with three identical envelopes. In one, place a teaspoon or packet of sugar; in the second, a teaspoon or packet of artificial sweetener; in the third, a couple of almonds or a spoonful of sesame seeds or sunflower seeds. Seal the envelopes; mix them up.

2. Test for Normal Resistance, as described on page 96.

3. Without telling your partner what substances are in the envelopes, give him one envelope to hold in the hand that's down at his side. Test his extended arm for resistance. Repeat with the other two envelopes, noting which test strong and which test weak. (One way is to number them and note the results on a piece of paper.)

4. Have your partner test you on each envelope.

5. Open all envelopes and share the results.

The vast majority of people will test weak on the sugar and artificial sweetener, but strong on the almond, sunflower seed or sesame seed. Research done on sugar and saccharin products correlates convincingly: These substances, and foods containing them, are unhealthy for most people. (See p. 71-92.) For confirmation, test again with each substance, one at a time, in the mouth.

As kinesiology demonstrates, the body knows instantly what is good or not good for it. As Dr. Diamond remarks, "The body is the best biochemist."[32] Unfortunately, we have learned to consume and enjoy foods that are terrible for our systems. As a matter of fact, the body can become addicted to foods that are not good for it, creating vicious cycles and much damage to health. Sugar addiction as discussed pages 79-80 is an example.

food allergy testing

Each individual's body chemistry and sensitivity (or allergy) to various foods is different. One can have subtle "allergies" or toxic reactions that one is not aware of: a food may lower one's immunity to certain illnesses, cause depression or fatigue, headaches (it is well known that a percentage of migraine sufferers are simply allergic to chocolate), stomach distress, etc. "Hyperactivity" in children is often an allergic reaction to sugar and chemical additives in foods (See pp. 73-74). Other common food allergies include milk, eggs, and wheat.

Test for food allergies by placing a food (it can be placed in a napkin) in one hand, and testing the other arm for resistance. (Remember to test for Normal Resistance, with both hands empty, first.) When the arm goes down easily, it means the food being tested is not good for the person being tested. For confirmation, test again, with the food placed in the person's mouth.

Eliminate foods that weaken you in these tests from your diet for several weeks. Then have yourself tested again; the results will probably be better because your body has had a rest from those foods. You may be able to occasionally eat an offending food without seriously weakening your energies, but don't eat it more frequently than once every three or four days. Keep having yourself tested. Some foods may be too weakening for you to eat--ever.

I, personally, suffered from recurring gastroenteritis for years. I tried many remedies including medical tests and treatments, special diets, and non-traditional healing methods such as acupuncture, massage, etc. No remedy eliminated the problem. When I learned about kinesiology, I had myself tested and discovered I tested weak on 6 or 7 foods. Since I stopped eating these foods, I've had no more stomach distress.

If your children are eating (or demanding) a lot of sweets and other junk foods, test them. The technique will graphically show them how bad these products are for them. It may help you to persuade them to eat more healthful foods. (Children more than adults tend to believe and follow through on what they can plainly see; after testing them, you may find them scoffing at the TV commercials that described Wonder (white) Bread and Sugar Frosted Flakes as "helping to build strong, healthy bodies.")

vitamin supplements

As mentioned previously in the section on vitamins (p. 87), I believe vitamin supplements are necessary for us to achieve optimum health in our modern enviroament, even if we eat healthful, fresh foods. However, most people are confused about what supplements they should take, in what quantity, and whether the supplements should be natural or synthetic. Using kinesiology testing to "ask" the body about its needs, all of these questions can be answered.

Make your mind "a blank." Have your partner test you for Normal Resistance. Hold the vitamin you are testing in your other hand, and have your partner test you again. If your arm goes down easily, it can mean one of several things:

1. The vitamin may be synthetic and your system will function better on natural vitamins. Try testing yourself with a natural version of the vitamin.

2. The brand being tested may have an *ingredient* to which you are allergic. Test other brands of the same vitamin. If it's a multiple vitamin, test the individual components.

3. The dosage of this supplement may be too strong for your system. Test a smaller dosage.

Here is how to test for the quantity you should be taking. Start with a vitamin on which you've already tested strong. Add one more of that vitamin to your hand and test again. Keep adding more tablets or capsules, and testing, until your arm tests weak. At that point, you've exceeded your maximum dosage. Reduce the number of pills or capsules until you are testing very strong again. That is your maximum daily dosage.

Test yourself again, periodically (every few months or when your life has changed greatly), on all the supplements you routinely take. One's needs change over a period of time, particularly at times of increased emotional or physical stress, when the body consumes many more vitamins in defending against illness and other stress effects.

I did an interesting "in the blind" experiment using vitamins with a medical doctor friend. He had tested strong on one supplement, weak on another. We wrapped them in paper so we could not tell them apart. A third person, a nuclear physicist, mixed them up, out of our view. The doctor would take one package in his hand, holding it behind his back. I would turn around, face him, and test his extended arm. If he tested strong, I said he was holding Supplement X, and if he tested weak, I named Supplement Y. The physicist checked, and recorded the results.

I was correct 18 out of 20 times, a 90% accuracy rate. Participants and observers of the test concluded that something significant had occurred, though they were at a loss to explain it through their usual medical or scientific understanding.

testing your workplace

Remember how much a simple smile or frown could affect your energy level? Since we are taught to suppress our emotions, particularly at work, it's likely that you are having negative (and positive) reactions to all sorts of things at work without being aware of them or taking them seriously. Kinesiology testing is an excellent way to find out which people, events, and parts of your physical environment at work are strengthening you, and which ones are weakening you and increasing your stress.

1. Have someone test you as you think about each of your co-workers, superiors, subordinates, and frequent business contacts one at a time.

2. How do you spend your time at work? Have yourself tested while thinking about each of your major tasks.

Besides rearranging your work relationships and your duties as much as possible to emphasize the ones that strengthen you the most, there are remedies to counteract the weakening effect of aspects that are negative for you (see p. 110).

If your entire job is negative and you can't make changes in it, you might want to consider a career or workplace change.

3. You can also test elements in your physical environment—your decor, paintings, colors, plants, etc.—just by looking at or touching the thing you're interested in, while your partner tests your arm for resistance.

The next two sections deal with environmental aspects that can have a profound impact on workplace well-being: lighting and music.

fluorescent lights

Test your partner for Normal Resistance (see p. 96). Then find a fluorescent light. Have your partner look directly at it while you test her arm. She will test weak.

What your partner has experienced is the effect of "cool white" fluorescent tubing, which comprises most of the fluorescent lighting used in offices. The book *Health and Light*, by John Ott (Berkeley, California: Devin-Adair, 1973), documents the ways in which the combination of light waves in "cool white" fluorescents adversely affects our systems. Office workers report feelings of sleepiness, despair, nervousness, irritability, nausea and dizziness—all of which disappear when lighting is changed to incandescent or a special type of "daylight balanced" or "full spectrum" fluorescent bulb.

Ott was the filmmaker who produced the original Walt Disney time lapse films of flowers. He shot one frame every few minutes over a period of days; when the film was sped up, the flowers unfolded gracefully before the viewer's eyes. Ott discovered that different colors of light affect plants in different ways. Some colors or combinations are beneficial; others are deleterious. Ott then turned to researching the effects of light on humans. He reports a variety of startling improvements that occur when full spectrum fluorescent lights are introduced into a work situation. Industries have experienced a 25 percent increase in productivity.[33] In colleges, students' abilities to concentrate and to retain information have risen measurably; and in grammar schools, children who have been hyperactive have suddenly become calm and cooperative when the lighting is changed.[34]

Most people spend at least eight hours a day working, studying, or travelling under "cool white" fluorescent bulbs. It's hard to tell how much fatigue, boredom, and illness—on and off the job—results from unhealthy lighting.

To complicate matters, building codes in most cities require minimum lighting levels in commercial buildings which are far higher than what is needed for optimum eyesight. The American Society of Heating, Refrigeration, and Air Conditioning Engineers (ASHRAE) recommends lighting levels 20 to 30 percent *below* what most building codes require.[35] Lighting industry and electrical utility lobbies have successfully persuaded legislators in many localities to increase minimum lighting requirements on an almost yearly basis. In Atlanta, GA, one of the office buildings of the Georgia Power Company is so heavily lit that air-conditioners must be turned on in the winter to counteract the heat from the light fixtures![36] This situation not only wastes energy and money; it increases the headaches, fatigue and eyestrain caused by "cool white" fluorescent lights. lights.

Changing the lighting in schools, offices, factories, and public places to full spectrum lighting may be one of the most effective single things you can do to reduce stress.

For more information about full spectrum fluorescent lights, contact the manufacturers:

Armor Enterprises
Dept. CAC
P. O. Box 15411
Plantation, FL 33318
(305) 583-2852

Luxor Lighting Products, Inc.
Dept. G
7606 East Linden Place
Parma, OH 44130
(216) 741-2266

music

Music, like everything else in the environment, can be beneficial or detrimental to us. Dr. Diamond has found that much of contemporary rock music (though not *all* of it) weakens the body's energy system. According to him, the weakening effect seems to be caused by a certain beat that is common in rock music, a rhythm of "da-da-DA," which repeats in such a way that the song almost seems to stop momentarily after each measure (after each "DA"). (In poetry, this is known as an anapestic beat.)

Dr. Diamond has found correlations between this type of sound and a phenomenon called "switching" in which the left side and right side of the brain cease working together in balance. Many innocuous everyday activities can cause "switching," as Diamond explains in his book. When switching has occurred, one side of the brain is working too hard. Thinking or solving problems becomes more difficult, and the person experiences increased stress. Since this is such a common state, most people don't notice these effects consciously, except for a vague sense of confusion, discomfort or fatigue. The feeling may be "There's too much going on here," or "I have more demands on me than I can deal with."[37]

Not all rock music weakens us. Test it for yourself. Have a partner test you for Normal Resistance, then test again while you're listening to a particular record. You can test your whole record collection this way, to see which music actually strengthens you or is neutral for you, and which music weakens you. If music is played in your workplace, test some of the people there to see how it is affecting them. Perhaps you can change the music, or have it changed, to something that has a strengthening effect, test it and see.

Dr. Diamond cites the following example:

"One factory in particular, a manufacturing and repair plant for sophisticated electronic equipment, where concentration and clear-headedness are essential, was playing a great deal of rock on its continual music broadcast system. It was recommended that this be eliminated. The management changed to different music and found to their delight an immediate increase in productivity and an equally pleasing decrease in errors, even though the employees were quite vocal about their dissatisfaction at having their favorite music removed."[38]

This anecdote illustrates the fact that people can become addicted to music that is unhealthy, just as we can become addicted to unhealthy foods. From birth, we are exposed to so many things that are unhealthy or stressful that our bodies can become accustomed to the stresses and the state of disease, so that we actually crave negative stimuli as much or more than we crave positive stimuli.

Yet, people who investigate what would be healthy for them, and discipline themselves to eat it, do it, use it, generally find after a period of time that they feel better than they have ever felt in their lives. Their bodies become less confused and more instinctively sensitive to anything unhealthy, so that they find they can "taste" artificial additives or colorings in foods; they feel uncomfortable or ill when they eat, drink, or smoke something unhealthy; and when something in the environment lowers their energy level or dampens their spirits, they generally notice it immediately because of the contrast with their now-typical sense of well-being.

If you own or manage a business and you want to change the music, the food served in the lunchroom, or anything else that directly affects employees, the best procedure is to meet with them, explain and discuss the change and its expected benefits, show them the kinesiology testing themselves, and make the change on a trial basis. People are much more likely to cooperate with this approach than with having changes forced on them, even "for their own good."

Recently, some composers have begun to use kinesiological testing to make sure their music is strengthening. One such composer is Steven Halpern, Ph.D. He describes as "anti-frantic" the series of compositions he designed especially to be relaxing and energizing.

Also, Dr. Diamond has developed the Biological Harmonics series of cassette tapes, designed to strengthen the body's energy system. If you cannot locate Dr. Halpern's or Dr. Diamond's music in your local record store, write for further information to: Jerry Teplitz Enterprises, 4317 Tillman Drive, Virginia Beach, VA 23452.

warning: about digital music

More and more recorded music is being edited using digital equipment before it is transferred finally to record or tape. Digital equipment breaks the sound into millions of tiny bits of electronic information. This allows each bit to be edited separately, so that one note from one voice or instrument can be deleted, made louder or softer, speeded up or slowed down, raised or lowered in pitch, echoed, etc. Thus, digital editing is being heralded as a technical breakthrough, a great boon to the recording industry, since it allows easier, more exact, more controllable editing.

When the electronic bits are put back together as music, your brain will not consciously tell you that it is listening to bits of sound glued together. You will think you hear a continuous tone. However, the body knows differently--immediately.

All digital recordings have a very weakening effect on our energy, no matter what style the music is. Try this. Get a regular recording of a piece of music on which you test strong. Find a digital recording (they are generally labeled as such) of the same piece of music. Have your resistance tested with each.

Digital recording is becoming more and more widespread. Much of the music played on the radio may soon be digitally edited. If your announcer mentions that a digital recording is playing, test for yourself. The negative impact of digital music on your energy system will outweigh any positive benefit you might otherwise get from the music.[39]

If you are concerned about this, let the radio stations and record companies know that you won't buy or listen to digital. If people won't buy it, they won't make it. In addition to the information presented here, and the evidence you can compile through your own kinesiology testing (test a local disc jockey and see the surprise!), further reports on the subject will be published by *The Diamond Report* newsletter (see Bibliography).

One alternative in the workplace is to install a stereo system with turntable or tape player, and pre-test what is played on it.

the meridian test

1. Test for Normal Resistance (See p. 96). While your partner keeps the position, arm extended, use one of your hands to trace a straight line in the air along one side of his body, from your partner's eye to his foot.

2. Immediately retest the resistance in your partner's arm by telling him to resist as you push down. The arm will usually go down much more easily than normal. Surprised?

3. Have your partner extend his arm again. This time, trace a line in the air upwards, from your partner's foot to the eye, without touching him.

4. Immediately retest your partner's ability to resist. Do you find your partner testing normal again?

5. Switch; have your partner test you.

The vast majority of people test weak when you've run your hand from the eye to the foot, and strong when you've traced from the foot to the eye.

These results correspond to the body's acupuncture meridians, also known as "energy lines." The remarkable success of acupuncture in curing a variety of mental and physical disturbances and in improving general health is due to its precise mapping and understanding of the relationships among these meridian pathways. (See also the chapter on shiatsu, p. 14.)

Meridian lines run in certain directions. The stomach meridian runs from the foot to the eye. Tracing that path strengthens that meridian, and the body. Yet, tracing that meridian in the opposite direction weakens both the line and the body, as you saw clearly when you tric it with your partner.

Try testing for the spleen meridian. Test for Normal Resistance (See p. 96). Now, with your hand at partner's waist level, trace a line though the air from one side of her body to the area of her belly button—just a short stroke. Immediately test resistance. As you push on the extended arm, it should go down easily. One common activity that cuts the spleen meridian—constantly—is ironing clothes. No wonder it is so fatiguing!

To re-strengthen the spleen line, do a circular massage on the area you traced with your hand, moving from side to belly button. You must actually touch the person this time. Immediately re-test your partner's resistance. The extended arm will usually stay level.

how kinesiology works

Suppose we accept the unfamiliar premise that our bodies have these energy pathways—meridians—and that moving in certain directions can be bad for us. A question remains: How can these meridians be affected when our bodies are not even touched?

One explanation is found in the research of Kirlian photography, developed in the 1940's. A person stands near a high-frequency electrical field, while a photographic plate is held next to part of the body, for instance, a hand. When developed, the photograph reveals that the whole hand seems to be made of colored light—in patterns resembling flares, clouds, skyscapes, and the like. A band of light, sometimes several inches deep, extends out from the body part. Painstaking research has led Kirlian photographers to conclude that the light and color comprise an energy band, emanating from the body, as individual as a fingerprint.[40]

In fact, any person or animal, plant, or other living thing photographed in this manner will reveal such an aura. Could this simply be a picture of the electricity being transmitted through the object or body? No, because each person's aura is different, and because the aura changes radically depending on what the person is doing, thinking, feeling, and the state of the person's health at the time of the photograph. Significantly, inanimate objects or once-living things that have been dead longer than a few hours do not show up in Kirlian photographs. Even metals that are electrical conductors do not produce Kirlian images.[41]

Researchers are compiling data which correlates changes in the color and shape of the energy field with specific physical and psychological states (such as cancer, depression, etc.), so that Kirlian photography can be used as a medical diagnostic tool.

The Kirlian process reveals that every living thing emanates and is surrounded by a tangible, physical energy body. The mild electrical charge illuminates this invisible energy the way a sunbeam illuminates tiny dust particles which are normally invisible in the air. Thus, every living thing gives off unique, perceivable energy—and this energy *does* visibly react to internal and external stimuli.

Our brains make billions of unconscious calculations and translations every day to tell us what is going on around us; these calculations include information from our "sixth sense" (perceptions of the energy and emotions of other people and things around us), in addition to information from our eyes, ears, nose, taste, and the conscious aspects of touch. You may also be aware of this "sixth sense" when you suddenly "look up" or look around just in time to avoid a collision or mishap of some sort. What has probably happened is that your energy body and the energy body of whatever you were about to collide with started to cross or mingle. They "bumped" first.

Perhaps it is also our energy bodies that perceive and "read" the fact that there is sugar or *some* weakening substance in an envelope we're holding, just as our eyes perceive (so our brains can interpret) that we are seeing "book" or "desk" or "car."

Your energy body is directly affected by everything happening, inside and outside you. It appears that, properly understood, a person's energy body is a detailed picture of everything the person is experiencing at a given moment—physical, mental, emotional, spiritual.

Evidence shows that touching the energy body can have the same effects as touching the person's body *directly*. This is why you can "cut" your partner's meridian lines just by tracing in the air next to her. The process is similar to what happens when a station is coming in quite clearly on your car radio and, as you drive along, a second station begins to interfere. Another analogous situation is created by placing a mganet near an electrical wire. The magnet will measurably interfere with the flow of current, even though this is not visually apparent.

The impact on a meridian line is the same: you can't see it, but the body knows it immediately.

A friend of mine applied this in his weightlifting. Recall that the stomach meridian (actually a pair of them) runs from each foot to the eye above it, and that stimulating it in this direction is strengthening. In his traditional workout, this man had always lifted and lowered his dumbbells very close to his body. I explained to him that with every time he lifted the dumbbells up he was strengthening this meridian, but that every time he lowered them, he was probably weakening himself. So, he tried keeping the dumbbells close to his body on the upstroke, and extending his arms out to the sides, *away* from his body, on the downstroke. He reported immediate improvement: he was able to exercise longer, and felt his workout was easier.

Our meridian lines may be cut frequently during the day in normal interactions. When you pass someone in the hallway or in an elevator, one of you may move your arm in such a way that it cuts the other's spleen meridian. Normally, the body will readjust the energy imbalance. (See section on The Role of the Thymus, page 112.) However, since this may be happening all day long, it can contribute to an overall pile-up of stresses that leave the body fatigued and unable to adjust by the end of the day.

One way to prevent fatigue is to take several "meridian line strengthening breaks" throughout the day. Simply trace the lines from each foot to the eye above it several times, touching or not touching your body, as you wish. Try it for a few days and see if you feel less tired at the day's end.

These facts are offered to give you an understanding of the total picture of stresses you may be undergoing during a typical day, so you can take steps to strengthen yourself and recover from them. This should *not* be interpreted as a general recommendation to stay away from other people at work! Positive contact--especially smiles, warmth, hugs--can be highly strengthening. This is discussed at greater length in other sections of this chapter.

changing your energy: overcoming stress

There are several techniques you can use to alter the way in which stress affects you. Besides meditation, deep breathing and yoga, which are described in other chapters, there are exercises and habits discovered through kinesiological research that specifically strengthen and balance our energy systems. Among them are meridian line strengthening, turning your mind to positive thoughts, and smiling, which I've already mentioned. (Positive thinking and smiling are not accomplished by repressing or ignoring incidents that bother you and the feelings that follow. Rather, negative feelings should be faced, examined, understood, and left behind. Though this may not be easy, many of the techniques in this book will help. We will elaborate on this later in the chapter.)

our energy button

First, do the following test. Later, I'll explain what occurred. You'll need a packet of sugar.

1. Test your partner for Normal Resistance, as described on page 96.
2. Give her the packet of sugar to hold as you test her arm again. It should go down easily.
3. Tell your partner to place her tongue gently against the roof of her mouth, about ¼ inch behind the teeth.
4. Have her keep her tongue up while she holds the sugar and you test her again.

What happened? Most people's arms will stay up as long as the tongue is "up" against the roof of the mouth. As soon as the tongue is brought down, the negative effects of the sugar will return. The tongue, in that position at the roof of the mouth, acts as an energy button or switch.[42]

Placing the tongue up is analogous to turning on a light switch. Until the switch closes the electrical circuit, no electricity can flow through the system. Similarly, the tongue at the roof of the mouth closes the body's internal circuitry, allowing the energy to flow. In a sense, it is lighting up our lights.

Developing the habit of keeping the tongue at the roof of the mouth about ¼ inch behind the front teeth will negate many stress effects upon us. It's best to keep the tongue in this position at all times, except when talking or eating. Soon the tongue moves itself easily into this position and stays there, without conscious thought on your part. Many people notice that after they've tried this for a few days, their tongues habitually rest in the "up" position, and keeping the tongue down becomes an effort!

When your tongue is up, your meridian lines will not be weakened in the ways we previously described.

Keeping the tongue at the roof of the mouth can be noticeably beneficial in sports or in any physical activitiy. This is partly because different kinds of body movement—including specific movements used in sports—can strengthen or weaken our energy systems. Try this experiment:

1. Test your partner for Normal Resistance, as described on page 96.
2. Have your partner use the same arm you just tested to go through the motions of three tennis forehand strokes. Now test his ability to resist. You'll find he tests strong.
3. Have him do three backhand strokes with the same arm, and test again. He should test weak.

The backhand movement actually weakened his energy level. It is no coincidence that even most professional players say their backhand is their weakest stroke. The explanation is that the backhand is one type of movement that causes "switching"—an unbalancing of the working relationship between the left and right brain hemispheres.

Switching produces an unconscious confusion in the body, stress, and a weakening of energy. We have already mentioned that it can be triggered by some rock and roll music (p. 104). Among the other body movements that can "switch" a person are typical jumping jacks, in which arm and leg movements mirror each other exactly. (This is a "homolateral" movement.) A different type of jumping jack, in which arms are together while legs are apart, and vice versa, does not switch our brain hemispheres and, thus, is not weakening. (It is a "hetero-lateral" movement.) For an explanation of different types of movement and why they affect the brain in these ways, see *BK: Behaviorial Kinesiology,* or *Your Body Doesn't Lie.*

Retest your partner on the tennis backhand movement or after he's done three of the homolateral jumping jacks; but this time, have him put his tongue to the roof of his mouth while he's doing the movements. This time, his resistance should stay strong. The extra energy boost of the tongue's position negated the weakening effects of these body motions.

(If you are wondering if the strengthening effect could be "the power of suggestion," do a set of these tests without telling your partner what the tongue position is supposed to do.)

I suggested the tongue technique to a bicycle racer who was skeptical about its usefulness. Shortly thereafter, he became tired during a race, and tried the tongue position. He regained his energy and went on to win the race. Another man, a middle-aged runner who competes in 5-mile races, noticed a marked improvement in his racing time after he started keeping his tongue up all the time.

the role of the thymus gland

Certainly the stronger your energy system is, the better able you will be to deal with any stress aggravations that arise. A central role in the energy system is played by the thymus gland. Once thought by the medical profession to have no function in adults, the thymus is now known as the body's center of immunity and resistance. It "trains" lumphocytes—white blood cells that fight infection—to do their job; and it sends out hormones to help direct lymphocyte activity throughout the body.[43]

Thymus activity is central to the theory of cancer developed by Australian Nobel Prize winner, Sir MacFarlane Burnet. He states that, of the billions of new cells produced in the body each day, some will *always* be abnormal. Thymus-derived lymphocytes ("T" cells) can recognize and destroy these abnormal cells. *But,* if "T" cells are not activated by the thymus hormone, some abnormal cells may survive, lodge themselves somewhere in the body, and grow into cancer. Thus, the thymus gland is critical in cancer prevention.[44]

This theory is supported by the fact that cancer occurrence increases with age. Thymus activity in mammals *decreases* with age. (The antibody response of old mice is only about 5 percent that of young mice, Dr. Diamond reports.)

Each new piece of research on the thymus reveals it to be more important than the last. Recent findings show that the thymus gland not only heads up the immunological system, but also regulates the flow of energy throughout the body from moment to moment. It is the job of the thymus to both defend the body from illness and to repair (as best it can) the effects of stress.[45]

Thus, when a meridian line is "cut," the thymus will readjust the energy flow back to that line. By the end of the day, due to fatigue, the readjustment process is taking longer and longer after each incident of stress.

strengthening the thymus

The thymus gland is located about where the second button on a shirt would be located, in the center of the chest just below the collarbone. An inch or so below the hollow at the base of the throat, you will feel a slight bump; that's the thymus.

Tapping or thumping on this spot has a very beneficial effect on the entire body. Tapping the thymus will rapidly cancel out most stress effects. Tap the spot rapidly with your fingertips 10 to 15 times. Doing this routinely, five or six times a day, will assist you in successfully handling short term stress. The length of time during which the thymus will stay strong varies with the person and the types of situations one encounters. The more stressful the environment, the less time the benefit lasts.

To test the strength of your thymus, place two or three fingers on the thymus spot, touching the skin. Have someone test your other arm for resistance. If you test weak, tap or thump the thymus spot several times. Then have your arm tested again while your fingers are in place. Do you feel stronger?

You can do confirmation testing on the effects of different stimuli, like pictures, music, foods, thoughts, and various people, on your thymus in much the same way as you test their effects on your general energy level. If you want to know whether something actually weakens your thymus, (i.e., your stress-resistor and corrector) instead of just knowing whether it puts stress on your system—look at, think about, or in some way place on your body the thing being tested. At the same time, make sure your fingers are touching your thymus during the test. If your other arm tests weak, you know the stimulus is weakening your thymus.

You might try tapping your thymus several times and *immediately* re-testing anything on which you've tested weak. You will probably find yourself testing sudddenly strong. This is because the tapping has given your stress resistance equipment a boost.

Two kinds of supplements have the same strengthening effect on the thymus as tapping it. These tablets can produce immediate benefits if chewed or dissolved in the mouth. If swallowed, they take longer to work. Either will regulate stress effects for up to three or four hours.

The supplement known as Dismuscorb® is made from an enzyme extract of garden peas—superoxide dismutase. The Thymus Plus® supplement is composed of extracts from animal thymus glands. During kinesiology testing, a person who pops one of these tablets ino his mouth will immediately begin to test stronger on everything.

Among the positive reports I've received from people who have used these products was one from a woman who lost weight with the help of Dismuscorb. Her eating was stress related. Whenever she felt under stress, she took a Dismuscorb, which she found reduced her stress level and, thus, her desire to eat.

If you acquire either tablet, experience its effectiveness for yourself. Find a partner whose thymus gland tests weak. Have her chew some Dismuscorb or Thymus Plus, and retest her thymus. It should test very strong.

You might want to retest every hour or so to see how long the strengthening effect lasts.

Many people who have seen or experienced the effect of Dismuscorb or Thymus Plus in my seminars have reported difficulty in finding these supplements in their health food or drug stores. If you cannot find them on the market, write to Jerry Teplitz Enterprises, 4317 Tillman Drive, Virginia Beach, VA 23452.

handling emotional issues

Earlier in the chapter, you saw the vivid impacts of positive and negative thoughts and feelings. Negative thoughts diminish a person's strength, energy level, and stress resistance. Paradoxically, then, a person is *less capable* of handling some aggravation, touchy issue, or upsetting event when *already* preoccupied with a negative thought or reaction.

At the same time, the act of repressing or ignoring negative feelings without understanding them does not usually work too well. Repression, or denying one's own truth, takes tremendous amounts of energy. And the repressed feelings may still weaken you because they are stored somewhere in your body even if they aren't in your mind. The goal is to feel a sense of relaxation and well-being: You can let the feeling drift away because it's not important anymore.

Recognizing, accepting, and understanding your feelings will *allow* you to let them go—calmly and cheerfully—even though you may still need to take action on the situation that caused the feelings in the first place. In the case of pain, anger, insult, frustration, betrayal, etc., it is almost always helpful to take "a step back" from the feeling, to diminish the intensity, so that the feeling is not so overwhelming that you can't think about what it means. Many of the relaxation techniques in this book—meditation, yoga, deep breathing, etc., will relieve much of the intensity. Here's another technique.

1. Sitting in a comfortable position, close your eyes. Take several deep breaths, as described in the deep breathing exercise on page 11.

2. Turn your mind to some very positive or satisfying thought. Envision, for instance, someone you love, some activity you enjoy, a place you would like to be, a hope fulfilled.

3. Keep breathing deeply and slowly while you focus on that thought for several minutes.

This exercise will reduce the impact of stressful situations and (even) give you an energy boost. Done several times a day, it will allow you to feel less fatigue at the day's end.

Here's another technique, to do with a partner, from the book, *Touch for Health*, by John Thie, D.C. (Marina del Rey, California: De Vorss, 1973):

1. Test your partner for Normal Resistance. Now, have your partner think of some problematic, confusing or upsetting emotional issue. Test his extended arm; it will go down easily.

2. Place your fingers on your partner's forehead, on the frontal lobes. These are sometimes felt as slight bulges on both sides of the forehead, between the eyebrows and hairline. Have your partner think about and visualize the emotional situation in as much detail as possible.

3. Continue gently touching the forehead points for up to 10 minutes.

Frontal Lobes

4. You'll know you've succeeded when you retest your partner's extended arm while he thinks of the same emotional situation and his arm stays strong.

With the emotionality of the thought reduced, it will be easier for him to confront the situation and deal effectively with it.

what if you test strong on everything?

Occasionally, you may find a person who tests strong on everything. This person's arm will not test weak with sugar, saccharin, flourescent lights, frowns, touching the thymus, etc. This means that the person's life energy is not being affected by the stresses around her. (Note—it doesn't mean the person never feels bad about anything; it just means that her body, thymus, and energy system are dealing with these feelings without being weakened.)

In an audience of several hundred people, I generally find only four or five people like this.

We can, however, develop this trait. Testing strong on everything should be a goal for all of us.

Following the techniques in this section—positive thoughts, smiles, strengthening the meridian lines, keeping the tongue against the roof of the mouth, listening to strengthening music, tapping the thymus, taking Dismuscorb or Thymus Plus—will help you get to the point where you, too, will test strong on everything.

sex and relaxation

Sex is an ingrained part of our culture. It is used to sell everything from chewing gum to automobiles. It appears in newspapers, on television and in the movies. However, sex is rarely depicted or recommended as a form of relaxation.

Sex can be both relaxing and energizing if a particular method called tantra yoga is followed.

Tantra yoga is an ancient Eastern technique. One of the main aspects is that the sex act is performed without the male having an ejaculation. This means that love-making can go on for long periods of time. In "Western" style sex, the act is over once the male has ejaculated. He has lost the energy to continue. Without an ejaculation, the male can continue to relate while the energy level continues to build. The result will be an increase in the energy both partners feel, much more than during "regular" sex.

Relaxation also occurs, because the physical movements are much slower in tantra yoga. Instead of looking for peaks of excitement through rapid movements, the partners are seeking valleys of relaxation through slower and easier movements. There is no rush to orgasm. You can imagine it as strolling through a beautiful meadow on a Sunday afternoon.

For the woman, enjoyment is actually increased because the length of time and the stimulation is increased. The woman can actually have as many orgasms during tantra as she desires. The orgasms the woman experiences increase the energy level of both partners. The man may find himself having orgasms—release of tension through his entire body —without ejaculating. The partners will not tire, or will be very slow to tire, because there is no tension and pushing for these experiences. It is more like letting a wave wash over you.

The end results are deep relaxation and energizing.

A man who ordinarily rolls over and goes to sleep after sex will find he can instead continue to be active and relate to the woman. Even a man who doesn't habitually fall asleep will find he has more energy than he would usually after sex.

Another benefit of tantra is that it lets each partner feel and experience the other more fully. Ordinarily, when one is enjoying sex, one is mainly conscious of the feelings in one's own body. With tantra, the length of the act and the slowness allow each partner to experience what the other is feeling . . . to really sense what is happening in the other's body. It is a very conscious sort of merging.

Tantra yoga should be done with a partner you care about. There must be increased communication between the partners. You need to be clear with each other on expectations and on the actual movements which are taking place—how does this feel . . . would something else be better. This results in the development of a deeper rapport and understanding between the partners.

Success in tantra depends greatly on the male's attitude. He must change his focus from intense movement to reach orgasm to one of slowing and lengthening the sex act. Reducing the competitive attitude many men bring to sex is an important step in allowing the relaxation from tantra yoga to flow in. The woman, too, must measure "success" differently, as it is not having the man achieve orgasm.

Here are some guidelines which will aid in developing tantra yoga for yourself and your partner:

1. *Keep breathing.* Instead of "panting", you need long, deep breaths that fill your body. As I discussed in the deep breathing section (pp. 11–

12), deep breathing keeps you relaxed, and keeps you from tensing your muscles. By continuing to breathe, you will begin to experience the valleys of relaxation of tantra.

2. Keep the movement slow. **Movement is necessary for the man to maintain an erection; however, too much movement can stimulate an ejaculation. (It's all right for the man to ejaculate once every few times he does tantra.)**

3. *Movement doesn't have to be constant.* It's OK to stop and rest. If the man is feeling too stimulated, just rest in the position you're both in at that moment.

4. *Explore all kinds of movements.* Touch, massage, caress . . . do anything that feels pleasurable.

5. *After becoming familiar with the technique, some couples have found they enjoy having discussions or even reading to each other during tantra.*

6. *Change positions.* Avoid positions in which the man is receiving a lot of stimulation; for example, with the man on top of the woman. Since you will be communicating throughout the experience, talk about which positions feel helpful and which do not. Be willing to experiment.

Don't be upset if you are not completely successful the first time you try tantra. It takes practice and requires a period of adjustment to become adept at it, and to feel all the benefits. The result, though, will be rewarding, as you open yourself to new vistas in your sexual relationships and new avenues of relaxation in your life.

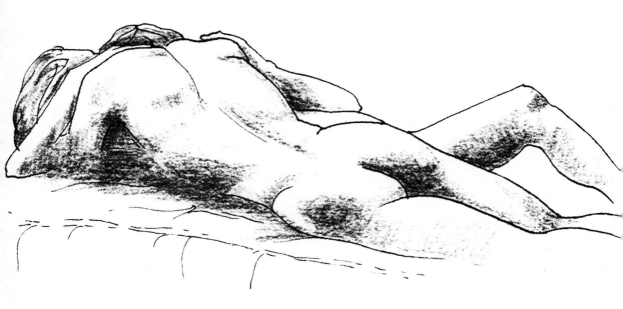

footnotes

Meditation
1. Denise Denniston and Peter McWilliams, *The TM Book: How to Enjoy the Rest of Your Life*, Price Stern & Co., 1975.
2. *Ibid.*

Nourish Thyself
1. Roger J. Williams, M.D., "Fighting for Real Nutrition," *Cosmopolitan*, June, 1973, p. 187.
2. *Prevention* magazine, Sept., 1974, p. 82–84.
3. Donald H. Masters, D.D.S., "The Sour Side of Sugar," *Journal of the Society for Preventive Dentistry*, Jan.–Feb., 1975, p. 28.
4. Ben Feingold, M.D., *Why Your Child is Hyperactive*, Random House, 1974.
   William Crook, M.D., *Can Your Child Read? Is He Hyperactive?* Pedicenter Press, 1975.
5. Robert Rodale, "Three Ways to Use Vitamins," *Prevention*, June, 1975, p. 25–28.
6. Ruth Heyman, "Schizophrenics—How Are They Doing on Megavitamins?" *Prevention*, Feb., 1975, p. 110–119.
7. Joseph A. Emerson, "Cholesterol: The Most Misunderstood Nutrient," *Whole Life Times*, #39, mid-November/December 1984, p. 21.
8. *World Review of Nutrition and Dietetics*, Vol. 12, 1970.
9. Emerson, *op. cit.*, p. 23-25.
10. Masters, *op. cit.*, p. 23.
11. *Ibid.*, p. 23 and 28.
12. "Sugar: the 'Energy' Problem," advertisement by Erewhon, Inc., as published in *East West Journal* during 1974.
13. Masters, *op. cit.*, p. 26.
    E. Cheraskin, M.D., *Diet & Disease*, Rodale Press, 1968.
    John Yudkin, M.D., *Sweet and Dangerous*, Wyden Press, 1972.
14. Ann Ferrar, "How to Beat the Blood-Sugar Blues," *Whole Life Times*, #43, June 1985, p. 29. Also see E.M. Abrahamson, M.D., and A.W. Pezet, *Body, Mind, and Sugar*, Henry Holt & Co., 1951, p. 36.
15. Abrahamson and Pezet, *op. cit.*, p. 58-60.
16. *Ibid.*, p. 44–70 and 176–195.
17. *Ibid.*, p. 44–70 and 176–195.
18. *Ibid.*, p. 59.
19. Williams, *op. cit.*, p. 190.
20. Daniel Grotta-Kurska, "Here's What You should Know about Vegetarianism," *Today's Health*, Oct., 1974, p. 18–21.
21. Williams, *op. cit.*, p. 189.
22. Monda Rosenberg, "Honest Dark Loaf of Bread is a Slice of Health," in *Toronto Star*, Jan. 4, 1975, p. H-3.
    Jane Kinderlehrer, "Some Delicious Ways to Enjoy your Bran." *Prevention*, Apr., 1975, p. 131.

23. Kinderlehrer, *Ibid.*, p. 130–134.
24. *Ibid.*, p. 134.
25. *Ibid.*, p. 132 and 134.
26. Michael Clark, "Food Additives, Cancer & the Prevention System," *Prevention*, July, 1976, p. 140.
27. *Ibid.*, p. 140.
29. Bill Gottlieb, "The Way They Ate Was a Crime," *Prevention,* May 1979, p. 64-68; and "The Court Where Junk Food Goes on Trial," *Prevention,* May 1978, p. 52-59.
30. Stephen B. Hulley, M.D. *Journal of the American Medical Association (JAMA),* Nov. 21, 1977; cited in *Prevention,* Feb. 1978, p. 86-90.

Body Talk: Behavioral Kinesiology
31. John Diamond, M.D., *Your Body Doesn't Lie,* Warner Books, (NY), 1980, p. 43-52; or *BK: Behavioral Kinesiology,* Harper & Row (NY), 1978, p. 16-22. (Cited hereafter as *Your Body* and *BK,* respectively.)
32. *Your Body,* p. 172 or *BK,* p. 110.
33. John N. Ott, *Health & Light,* Pocket Books (NY), 1976, p. 114.
34. *Ibid.*, p. 192-194.
35. Arthur D. Little Co., *An Impact Assessment of ASHRAE Standard 90-95, p. 43-58.*
36. Nate Thayer, researcher; Boston Clamshell Coalition, 585 Mass. Ave., Cambridge, MA 02128.
37. *Your Body,* p. 77-81, or *BK,* p. 40-43.
38. *Your Body,* p. 164-165, or *BK,* p. 103-104.
39. John Diamond, M.D. and Jerome Mittelman, D.D.S., editors, "Destructive Sounds," in *BK for You,* Vol. 4, Winter 1980, p. 4. Available from the Institute of Behavioral Kinesiology (see Bibliography for address).
40. Lyall Watson, *Supernature,* Anchor Press/Doubleday (Garden City, NY), 1973, p. 141-151. Also see Ostander, S. and Schroeder, L., *Psychic Discoveries Behind the Iron Curtain,* Prentice-Hall (Englewood Cliffs, NJ), 1971.
41. *Ibid.,* p. 141-151.
42. *Your Body,* p. 66-68, or *BK,* p. 31-33.
43. *Your Body,* p. 38, or *BK,* p. 10; citing G.J.V. Nossal, *Antibodies and Immunity,* 2nd edition, Basic Books (NY), 1978, p. 97.
44. *Your Body,* p. 39-41, or *BK,* p. 11-13.
45. Joann Ellison Rogers, "Dr. Thymosin's Remedy," *Science,* March 1981, p. 73-76.

bibliography

Shiatsu

Yukiko Irwin; *Shiatsu;* J.B. Lippincott Co., New York, 1976.

Tokujiro Namikoshi; *Japanese Finger-Pressure Therapy*: *Shiatsu*; Japan Publications, Tokyo, 1972.

Toru Namikoshi; *Shiatsu Therapy, Theory & Practice;* Japan Publications, Tokyo, 1974.

Katsusuke Serizawa, M.D.; *Massage: The Oriental Method;* Japan Publications, Tokyo, 1972.

Katsusuke Serizawa; *Tsubo: Vital Points for Oriental Therapy;* Japan Publications, Tokyo, 1976.

Hatha Yoga

Richard Hittleman; *Yoga: 28-Day Exercise Plan*, Workman Publishing Co., New York; 1969.

B.K.S. Iyengar; *Light on Yoga*; Schocken Books, 1984.

Haruka Nagai; *MAKKO-HO: Five Minutes' Physical Fitness;* Japan Publications, Tokyo, 1972.

Masahiro Oki; *Healing Yourself Through Okido Yoga;* Japan Publications, Tokyo, 1977.

Masahiro Oki; *Practical Yoga;* Japan Publications, Tokyo, 1970.

Swami Rama; *Lectures on Yoga;* Himalayan International Institute of Yoga Science and Philosophy, Chicago, 1976.

Satchidananda; *Integral Yoga Hatha;* Holt Rinehart & Winston, New York, 1970.

Jess Stearn; *Yoga: Youth & Reincarnation;* Bantam Books, New York, 1965.

Swami Vishnudevananda; *The Complete Illustrated Book of Yoga;* Julian Press, New York, 1972.

Kohtaro Wada; *Ten Weeks to a Beautiful Figure;* Japan Publications, Tokyo, 1975.

Meditation and General Relaxation

Denise Denniston and Peter McWilliams; *The TM Book: How to Enjoy the Rest of Your Life;* Price Stern & Co., New York, 1975.

Dr. Samuel W. Gutwirth; *You Can Learn to Relax;* Hal Leighton Publishing Co., Beverly Hills, Calif., 1957.

Tomio Hirai; *Zen Meditation Therapy;* Japan Publications, Tokyo, 1975.

John White, editor; *Relax;* The Confucian Press, 1976.

John White, editor; *What Is Meditation?;* Anchor Books, Garden City, N.J., 1974.

Food & Nutrition

Herman & Cornelia Aihara; *Soybean Diet;* George Ohsawa Macrobiotic Foundation, Oroville, Calif., 1974

Nancy Albright; *The Rodale Cookbook;* Rodale Press, Emmaus, PA, 1977.

Adelle Davis; *Let's Cook It Right;* 1947, 1962, 1970.

   Let's Eat Right to Keep Fit; 1954, 1970.

   Let's Get Well; 1965.

   Let's Have Healthy Children; 1951, 1959, 1972.

   All books published by Harcourt Brace Jovanovich, New York.

Ellen Buchman Ewald; *Recipes for a Small Planet;* Ballantine Books, New York.

Marjorie Linn Ford; *The Deaf Smith Country Cookbook;* Collier Books, New York, 1977.

Carlton Fredericks; *Food, Facts and Fallacies;* Arco Publishing, New York, 1965.

Jacqueline Heriteau; *Grow It and Cook It;* Ballantine Books, New York, 1972.

Jean Hewitt; The *New York Times Natural Foods Cookbook;* Avon Books, New York, 1972.

Frank J. Hurd; *Ten Talents;* The College Press, Collegedale, Tenn., 1968.

Mollie Katzen; *Moosewood Cookbook* (recipes from Moosewood Restaurant, Ithaca, NY); Ten Speed Press, P.O. Box 7123, Berkeley, CA 94107; (415) 845-8414; $9.95 paper, $12.95 clothbound, +85¢ postage/copy. Also in bookstores.

Michio Kushi: *The Book of Macrobiotics;* Japan Publications, Tokyo, 1977.

Frances Moore Lappe; *Diet for a Small Planet,* 10th anniversary edition; Ballantine Books, New York, 1982.

Faye Martin; *Naturally Delicious Desserts & Snacks;* Rodale Press, Emmaus, PA, 1978.

Bill Shurtleff; *The Book of Tofu* (versatile soy protein that can be made to resemble meat; known in Chinese cuisine as "bean cake"); Autumn Press, Brookline, MA, 1975.

Anna Thomas: *Vegetarian Epicure;* Random House, New York, 1972; *Vegetarian Epicure Book II;* Knopf/Random House, New York, 1978.

Ten Talents Cookbook; Ten Talents Press, Box 86-A, Route 1, Chisolm MN 55719; single copy $9.95, 3+ copies $6.65 each, 30+ copies $6.45 each.

Also see "Resource material" section of text. p. 92.

122

Nutrition & Cancer

George Berkley; *Cancer: How to Prevent It and How to Help Your Doctor Fight It;* Prentice-Hall, Englewood Cliffs, NJ, 1978.

(There are many other excellent, recent books on this subject; check with a bookstore or consult a local holistic health center for guidance.)

"Body Talk": Behavioral Kinesiology

(Also see footnotes & references in the chapter.)

The Diamond Report newsletter, edited by John Diamond, MD and Jerry Mittelman, DDS; published by The Once Daily, Inc., POB 4018, Grand Central Station, NYC 10017.

"Exploring the Spectrum," a film by John Ott; available from International Film Bureau, 332 South Michigan Ave., Chicago, IL 60604; (312) 427-4545.

Institute of Behavioral Kinesiology, P.O. Drawer 37, Valley Cottage, NY 10989.

Sex and Relaxation

John Chang; *The Tao of Love and Sex: The Ancient Chinese Way to Ecstasy;* E. P. Dutton, New York, 1977.

Sondra Ray; *I Deserve Love;* Les Femmes Press, Millburne, CA, 1976.

Ashley Thirleby; *Tantra: The Key to Sexual Power & Pleasure;* Dell Publishing Co., New York, 1978.

Magazines covering Holistic Health, Nutrition, & Lifestyle

(This is just a sampling of the many good publications on the market. Look for them in bookstores, health food stores, newsstands, or subscribe directly.)

East West Journal, 17 Station St., Brookline, MA 02146; (617) 232-1000. Monthly.

Prevention; see Resources, p. 92.

Vegetarian Times, 41 East 42nd St., Suite 921, New York, NY 10017; (212) 490-3999. 10 issues/year.

Whole Life Times, 18 Shepard St., Brighton, MA 02135; (800) 562-5017, (800) 772-0048, (617) 783-8030. 9 issues/year.

cross-reference index

This index will guide you to some, but not necessarily all, of the appropriate techniques for relieving pains, strengthening, relaxing and toning various parts of the body. If one method doesn't suit you, try another. However, don't try any exercise or treatment in a chapter until you've read the introduction to that chapter at least once. The index also includes various subjects that are discussed or mentioned in the book.

executives and associations applaud jerry teplitz' programs:

"What can I say...You were a smash! We have never had a turnout for an education session like we did for yours. They all loved it! You were one of the high points of our convention."

Peggie Hagan, Convention Manager
NATIONAL UTILITY CONTRACTORS ASSOCIATION

"I received considerable insight into methods of relieving stress. Fatigue is well accepted as a cause of poor decisions and aircraft accidents. Your presentation would seem a natural for airlines and other aviation organizations."

William H. Cox, Editor
Corporate Flight Magazine

"We have 600 plus employees who are walking around smiling warmly and powerfully. Never have I seen so many individuals so full of positive feelings."

Margaret S. McGinn, Personnel Director
RICES NACHMANS DEPT. STORES

"You could have heard a pin drop. You had our Annual Business and Management Meeting participants so entranced! As the highest rated speaker of our meeting, it's a pleasure to send our sincere thanks for a terrific job."

Barbara Klemm, Director of Conferences
CREDIT UNION EXECUTIVES SOCIETY

"Your program was the highlight of our meeting. We have had nothing but favorable comments on your program, and I am more than happy to recommend it to other organizations as a sure fire winner of a program."

John P. Seeley, President
SOCIETY OF ASSOCIATION EXECUTIVES

For information on having Dr. Teplitz speak to your group or organization, contact: Jerry Teplitz Enterprises, Inc., 228 N. Donnawood Dr., Ste. 204, Virginia Beach, VA 23452, Phone 800-777-3529 or 757-431-1317, Fax 757-431-1503, Email Info@Teplitz.com, Website www.Teplitz.com

YOUR MARKETPLACE: TOOLS FOR BETTER LIVING

SWITCHED–ON LIVING LEARNING - $150

This book, 2 - 45 minute video tapes and four-cassette tape album is the same program that is sold on the TV show by Dr. Jerry V. Teplitz. It offers a tremendous amount of information. While other people talk about the power of positive thinking, Dr. Jerry V. Teplitz gives you the experience. He shows you how completely powerful YOU really are and how to apply that to all aspects of your life. He also focuses on the three key factors involved in living longer healthfully--Nutrition, Exercise, and Attitude. You will understand the things you can do to place yourself in charge of your own life.

TRAVEL STRESS: THE ART OF SURVIVING ON THE ROAD $85

This exciting six-cassette album with workbook is designed to meet the needs of executives, managers, salespeople and anyone who spends time "on the road". Dr. Teplitz shares with you his proven travel techniques gathered from over 28 years spent traveling as a professional speaker.

POWER OF THE MIND (video)...$85

Learn how completely powerful your mind is. Using your mind, you can actually create the things you want. Viewers will experience the difference between positive and negative thinking, how to change thought patterns, and the effects of music on the mind, body and performance.

INSTANT HEADACHE RELIEF (video)..$85

Just about everyone gets them. Now, there is a technique that is 5,000 years old which is both safe and effective called Shiatsu, a Japanese finger pressure technique for pain relief .Using it you can eliminate a headache (or a hangover) in 11/2 minutes and migraines in 5 minutes. This video tape also covers stiff necks, and shoulder tension.

YOUR SELLING SUCCESS FORMULA (cassette tapes)...........................$65

This four-cassette tape album and self-assessment instrument allows you to become a more effective and successful salesperson by understanding your own selling behavior style as well as your clients' buying style. Companies have reported an increase in sales from 5-30%.

CREATING HIGH ENERGY WEB SITES AND PR MATERIALS. (video)..$85

Your web sites and pr materials have an impact on your readers and surfers. The question is it strengthening or weakening. If it's weakening you get unintended consequences. This live seminar will should you why and how you are impacting people and how to create a high energy impact.

PAR AND BEYOND: SECRETS TO BETTER GOLF (video)........................$85

This is a practical and dynamic video that shows you tools and techniques that immediately put you incharge of your game and will allow you to quickly and easily improve. You'll learn how to energize in seconds and refocus instantly.

SUBLIMINAL MUSIC

This series of cassettes and CDs was designed by Steven Halpern to contain a unique process which uses music and inaudible positive statements to allow the listeners to achieve successful changes in their lives. Tapes - $15.00, CDs - $19.00.

Achieving Your Ideal Weight   Accelerated Learning Enhancing Creativity Enhancing Success Enhancing Self-Esteem Attracting Prosperity Enhancing Creativity Health and Well-Being

To Order: Call 800 77-RELAX, 757 431-1317, FAX 757 431-1503, Website www.Teplitz.com

JERRY V. TEPLITZ

Jerry V. Teplitz is a graduate of Hunter College and Northwestern University School of Law; he received his doctorate in Wholistic Health Sciences from Columbia Pacific University. He formerly practiced as an attorney with the Illinois Environmental Protection Agency.

President of his own consulting firm for the past 28 years, Dr. Teplitz conducts seminars, lectures, and training programs for businesses, schools, and conventions in the areas of stress management, management and leadership development, and sales success. He is also a certified consultant for The Inscape Publishing Company.

Besides authoring *Managing Your Stress: How to Relax and Enjoy,* Dr. Teplitz has also written *Switched-On Living* and *Brain Gym for Business.* He has been the subject of articles in *Prevention* and other magazines. He has appeared on numerous radio and television shows throughout the United States and Canada. and has spoken to over 1,000,000 people.

Dr. Teplitz was honored in 1982 by his peers in the National Speakers Association when he was given the title of Certified Speaking Professional while the International Platform Association named him as a Top Rated Speaker. He's been listen in several editions of *Who's Who in America.*

SHELLY KELLMAN

Shelly Kellman was Senior Editor of *Whole Life Times* magazine. She is a free lance writer, photographer, graphic designer, publicist, and editorial consultant. Her articles have appeared in *Whole Life Times, New Age, In These Times,* Columbia University's *Journal of International Affairs,* and other publications. She has consulted or worked for the Illinois Department of Mental Health & Developmental Disabilities, the Cancer Prevention Center of Chicago, the Public Art Workshop (Chicago), the New York University School of Nursing, the Central America Education Fund (Boston), and numerous community and environmental organizations and private health professionals.